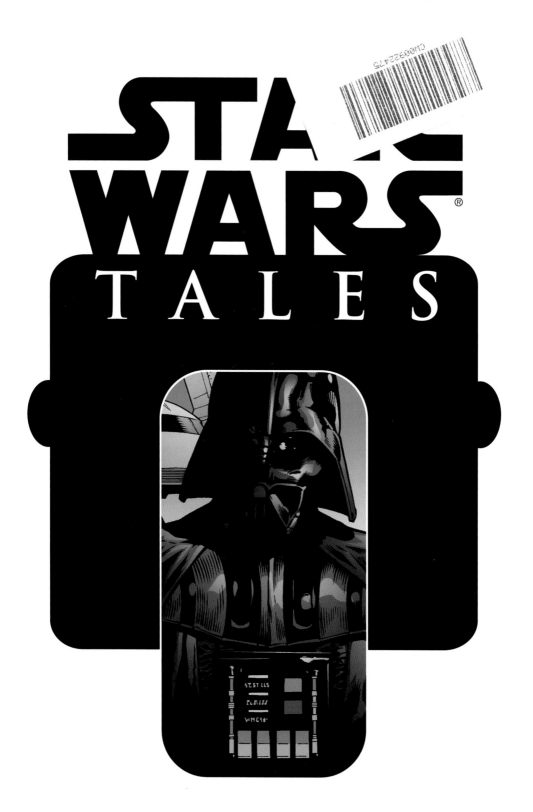

STAR WARS®

TALES

Volume 6

Dark Horse Books™

OLD REPUBLIC ERA
(25,000 - 1,000 BEFORE THE BATTLE OF YAVIN)

The Old Republic was the legendary government that united a galaxy under the rule of the senate. In this era, the Jedi are numerous, and serve as guardians of peace and justice. The *Tales of the Jedi* comics series takes place in this era, chronicling the immense wars fought by the Jedi of old, and the ancient Sith. The Events in these stories take place approximately four thousand years before *Star Wars*: Episode I *The Phantom Menace*.

SHADOWS AND LIGHT:005
Script / JOSHUA ORTEGA
Art / DUSTIN WEAVER
Colors / MICHAEL ATIYEH
Letters / MICHAEL HEISLER

UNSEEN, UNHEARD:027
Script / CHRIS AVELLONE
Art / DUSTIN WEAVER
Letters / MICHAEL HEISLER

RISE OF THE EMPIRE ERA
(1000 – 0 YEARS BBY)

In the waning years of the Republic, the galactic senate was rife with corruption and scandal, and saddled with a bureaucracy so immense that effective governing was nearly impossible. The ambitious Senator Palpatine caused himself to be elected Supreme Chancellor, and promised to reunite the galaxy under a New Order. This is the era of the prequel trilogy. The Events in these stories take place approximately six months prior to ten years after *Star Wars*: Episode I *The Phantom Menace*.

MARKED:033
Script / ROB WILLIAMS
Art / CULLY HAMNER
Colors / WIL GLASS
Letters / MICHAEL HEISLER

NOMAD:045
Script / ROB WILLIAMS
Art / BRANDON BADEAUX
Colors / DAN JACKSON
Letters / MICHAEL HEISLER

HONOR BOUND:127
Script / IAN EDGINTON
Art / STEVE PUGH
Colors / MICHAEL ATIYEH
Letters / MICHAEL HEISLER

INFINITIES
The events in this story take place outside established *Star Wars* continuity

FETT CLUB:149
Script / KEVIN RUBIO
Art / ROGER LANGRIDGE
Colors / WIL GLASS
Letters / MICHAEL HEISLER

STAR WARS® TALES

REBELLION ERA
(0 BBY - 5 ABY)

An outcry of resistance begins to spread across the galaxy in protest to the new Empire's tyranny. Cells of Rebellion fight back, and the Galactic Civil War begins. This is the era that contains the classic trilogy. The events in these stories take place approximately seven years before to five years after *Star Wars*: Episode IV *A New Hope*.

NEW JEDI ORDER ERA
(25+ ABY)

The Jedi Knights are now a hundred strong. The New Republic has signed a peace treaty with what little remains of the Empire. The galaxy is finally enjoying a peaceful respite from decades of war. It's at this time that a horrible alien menace invades the Republic from beyond known space. The Yuuzhan Vong lay waste to entire worlds in their scourge, as depicted in the continuing novels of The New Jedi Order. The events in this story take place approximately twenty-eight years after *Star Wars*: Episode IV *A New Hope*.

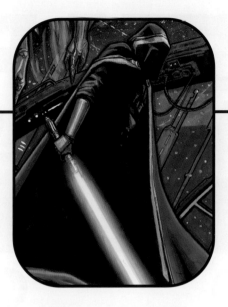

Publisher / MIKE RICHARDSON
Editor / JEREMY BARLOW
Assistant Editor / DAVE MARSHALL
Collection Designer / JOSHUA ELLIOTT
Art Director / LIA RIBACCHI

Special thanks to
JONATHAN RINZLER, LELAND CHEE,
and AMY GARY at Lucas Licensing

STAR WARS®: TALES — VOLUME 6

This book collects issues 21 through 24 of the Dark Horse
quarterly comic-book anthology *Star Wars: Tales*®.

Dark Horse Books™
A division of Dark Horse Comics, Inc.
10956 SE Main Street
Milwaukie, OR 97222

www.darkhorse.com
www.starwars.com

To find a comic shop in your area call the
Comic Shop Locator Service: (888) 266-4226

First edition: January 2006
ISBN: 1-59307-447-6

1 3 5 7 9 10 8 6 4 2
Printed in China

KORRIBAN? ARE YOU SERIOUS?

QUITE.

BUT THAT'S THE *SITH* HOMEWORLD. AND JUST YOU THREE?

YES -- JUST US THREE.

THIS IS A BEAUTIFUL BLADE...

SO WHAT WAS THE COUNCIL'S REASONING?

SIMPLE, REALLY. THEY NEED THIS FINAL HUNT DONE QUICKLY AND QUIETLY...

...AND WE'RE THE *BEST.*

TRUE, BUT... AREN'T YOU A BIT CONCERNED?

I AM A HUNTER, CALE. THIS IS WHAT I DO.

AND DURON AND SHAELA?

AS LONG AS THEY CAN CONTROL THEIR FEELINGS FOR ONE ANOTHER...

9

YES, THEY LEAVE FOR **KORRIBAN** TOMORROW.

HM. I STILL DON'T LIKE IT. THREE IS NOT ENOUGH. AND SENDING A QEL-DROMA TO KORRIBAN? THAT'S JUST ASKING FOR TROUBLE...

ULIC WAS THE ONLY QEL-DROMA WHO EVER FELL TO THE DARK SIDE, VROOK. WE CANNOT JUDGE DURON -- OR ANY JEDI -- BY THEIR BLOOD ALONE.

HOWEVER, I AGREE WITH YOU ON THE FIRST POINT. WE SHOULD SEND MORE JEDI ON THIS HUNT. MAYBE EVEN ONE OF US.

CORUSCANT DOES NOT WANT A LARGE PARTY OF JEDI ON KORRIBAN -- TOO MUCH RISK. THAT IS WHY THEY CHOSE THE THREE. I FEEL WE MUST ABIDE BY THE COUNCIL'S DECISION.

BUT WHAT IF THE COUNCIL IS *WRONG?* KORRIBAN IS AN EVIL PLACE. IT CAN CORRUPT EVEN THE *PUREST* JEDI.

THAT IS THE WAY OF THE ORDER.

YOUR POINT IS VALID, *BALA.* I HAVE SOME RESERVATIONS AS WELL. HOWEVER, AS QUAL SAID, WE MUST ABIDE BY THE COUNCIL'S DECISIONS -- AND HAVE *FAITH* IN THEIR WISDOM.

AFTER ALL, DURON, SHAELA AND GUUN HAN ARE OUR GREATEST HUNTERS...

...BUT WE WOULD LIKE SOME INFORMATION.

‹TERENTATEKS? THOSE THINGS THAT EAT FORCE BLOOD? SURE. IN FACT, I KNOW A HALF BREED *MASSASSI* WHO COULD TAKE YOU TO ONE.›

AND YOUR TERMS?

‹TELL YOU WHAT, *HUMAN*. YOU GET US THAT KILO OF SPICE WE WERE TALKING ABOUT... AND WE'LL MAKE SURE YOU GET YOUR BEAST.›

ANOTHER *TARISIAN* ALE? ARE YOU TRYING TO TAKE ADVANTAGE OF ME?

I'M OFFENDED BY THE QUESTION. OF COURSE I AM.

OH, GOOD...

"...I LOVE BEING EXPLOITED."

THIS PLACE IS SICK -- IT'S CHANGING US. WE'VE ALREADY BEEN HERE TOO LONG.

IT'S ONLY BEEN A WEEK -- AND WE ALREADY HAVE A GOOD LEAD ON A TERENTATEK. I'D SAY WE WERE DOING PRETTY WELL.

WELL? WE'RE RUNNING SPICE FOR THE UNDERWORLD, SEDUCING SITH APPRENTICES... YOU'VE SPOKEN OF INFILTRATING THE SITH ACADEMY...

IT WAS ONLY A SUGGESTION. GUUN HAN MAY HAVE ALREADY GOTTEN THE INFORMATION WE NEED.

AND IF HE DIDN'T? DO YOU KNOW ABOUT THE SITH ACADEMY TRIALS? ARE YOU REALLY PREPARED TO KILL AN INNOCENT -- TO VIVISECT A HUMAN BEING?

I DON'T WANT TO KILL ANYMORE, SHAELA! I'M SICK OF KILLING. SICK OF HUNTING. I'M SICK OF THE BLOOD...

DURON...

YOU DON'T UNDERSTAND -- WHEN I MAKE CONTACT, I HEAR THEIR THOUGHTS... THEY MAY BE EVIL, BUT THEY *THINK*...THEY HAVE A SPIRIT AND --

UNNGHH!

15

KASHYYYK. THREE DAYS LATER.

DURING MY TIME ON KORRIBAN, I HEARD OF A "GREAT BEAST" THAT LIVED IN THE **SHADOWLANDS**, BENEATH THE MILE-HIGH **WROSHYR** TREES OF KASHYYYK.

THE WOOKIEES TELL ME THAT THIS BEAST HAS KILLED MANY JEDI. IT CAN ONLY BE ONE THING. THE COUNCIL IS WISE, BUT THEY DID NOT SEE THIS. THEY ARE NOT OMNISCIENT.

IT IS UNFORTUNATE THAT DURON AND SHAELA DECIDED TO STAY ON KORRIBAN...

THE HUNT GOES ON.

...FOR IN THAT DARK PLACE THEIR PASSION WILL CONSUME THEM.

I WISH THAT I COULD HAVE SAVED THEM. I TRULY DO.

BUT I MUST NOT LET THE PAST HAUNT ME. THERE CAN BE NO REGRET.

IF MY MIND IS NOT CLEAR ON THIS HUNT...

...THEN I WILL SURELY SUFFER THE SAME FATE.

KORRIBAN.
THE VALLEY
OF THE SITH
LORDS.

DID
YOU...DID
YOU FEEL
THAT?

SOMETHING
IN THE FORCE...

HE...NO...
GUUN HAN --
HE'S GONE.

WHY DID
YOU HAVE TO
LEAVE, YOU
ARROGANT --?

WE ARE
JUST AS MUCH
TO BLAME AS
HE...

REST IN
PEACE, MY
FRIEND. YOU
WILL BE
MISSED.

WE'RE
CLOSE...GET
READY...

I'VE TRACKED THE WOUNDED TERENTATEK TO THE *TOMB OF NAGA SADOW*...

I NO LONGER CARE ABOUT *CODES* OR *COUNCILS*, *LIGHT* OR *DARK* SIDES. NONE OF THAT MAKES *SENSE* ANY MORE. ONLY *REVENGE* MAKES SENSE -- ONLY *ANGER*.

ONLY *BLOOD* CAN WASH THESE EMOTIONS FROM MY MIND.

MY LOVE IS *DEAD*. ALL I SEE IS *DARKNESS* BEFORE ME.

NOTHING MATTERS ANYMORE.

MASTER OOD, PLEASE *FORGIVE* ME...I HAVE *FALLEN* SO FAR.

"YOUR SOUL IS AS RADIANT AND PURE AS ANY I HAVE EVER KNOWN."

"YOU WILL ACCOMPLISH GREAT THINGS IN YOUR LIFE, SHAELA NUUR..."

"JUST REMEMBER TO ALWAYS STAY IN THE LIGHT."

"ALWAYS."

END

UNSEEN, UNHEARD

4000 YEARS BEFORE THE RISE OF THE GALACTIC EMPIRE. THE MID-RIM MIRALUKA COLONY OF KATARR.

THIS IS MY WORLD.

MY PEOPLE, THE MIRALUKA, SEE ITS BEAUTY NOT WITH THEIR EYES, BUT THROUGH THE FORCE.

THEY DO NOT SEE IT HAS LESS THAN AN HOUR TO LIVE.

KATARR WAS A WORLD FILLED WITH FORCE SENSITIVES, AND IT CALLED TO MY LORD.

ABOARD HIS DEAD SHIP, HE *HUNGERED* THROUGH THE FORCE, DREW SUSTENANCE FROM DEATH.

MY PEOPLE NEVER SAW HIS FACE WHEN HE STRUCK -- BUT THEY HEARD HIS *VOICE.*

WHEN MY LORD *SPOKE*, EVERY LIVING THING ON KATARR DIED.

THE DESTRUCTION OF KATARR ECHOED THROUGH THE FORCE, THE SCREAMING OF COUNTLESS LIVES.

AS THE MIRALUKA SEE LIFE THROUGH THE FORCE, WE CAN SEE DEATH AS WELL.

IT IS SAID THERE WERE NO SURVIVORS ON KATARR.

THAT IS BECAUSE MY LORD CAME FOR THE LAST ONE HIMSELF.

DAYS LATER, I AWOKE ON HIS SHIP, MY WOUNDS HEALED.

I DID NOT KNOW WHERE I WAS.

I DID NOT KNOW WHY HE HAD BROUGHT ME THERE.

I ASKED HIM WHY HE HAD SPARED ME.

AND ALTHOUGH HE SAID NOTHING, I SUDDENLY *KNEW* THE ANSWER.

IT WAS BECAUSE HE WANTED MY PEOPLE, AT LAST, TO *SEE.*

THE END

BUT NOT WELL ENOUGH.

SILUS... DON'T --

THEY USE THE FORCE FOR SPORT HERE, FOR FINANCIAL GAIN. IT IS A TAWDRY VENUE WHERE AMATEURS WITH LIMITED ABILITY FIGHT ONE ANOTHER.

SNAP!

BUT, FOR WHAT? MONEY? ACCLAIM? THESE THINGS ARE DUST ON THE SHOES OF THE RIGHTEOUS.

THESE...ANIMALS KNOW NOTHING OF DISCIPLINE. OF DUTY.

THEIR ACTIONS DEFILE US.

AND WHO MIGHT YOU BE?

A MESSENGER.

GREETINGS, SILUS. YOUR ABILITIES ARE IMPRESSIVE. I HAVE WATCHED YOU. YOU HAVE GREAT POTENTIAL.

YOU COULD BE OF USE TO ME.

SEARCH YOUR FEELINGS AND YOU WILL SENSE MY POWER.

NOT BAD. A DECENT NIGHT'S TAKE. THE MONEY KEEPS ROLLING IN.

MAYBE ONE DAY I'LL MAKE IT OFF THIS HOLE.

OR PERHAPS YOUR STORY ENDS HERE.

YES...

IF YOU WISH TO TAKE HIS PLACE... YOU WILL KILL HIM.

BUT FIRST... YOU MUST PROVE YOURSELF TO ME.

I ALREADY HAVE AN APPRENTICE. HE STANDS BEFORE YOU NOW.

YOU COULD BE SO MUCH MORE. I COULD TEACH YOU. GUIDE YOU. MAKE YOU MORE POWERFUL THAN YOU HAVE EVER DREAMED.

MASTER...?

39

THERE ARE PLACES IN THE GALAXY THAT ARE GRAND AND IMPORTANT.

WHERE ACTIONS AND DECISIONS CREATE FATE AND WRITE HISTORY.

THE MAJORITY OF US...WE NEVER SEE THOSE PLACES.

OUR NAMES WILL NOT BE REMEMBERED IN THE DAYS TO COME.

BUT WE STILL HAVE OUR STORIES.

THE OUTER RIM.

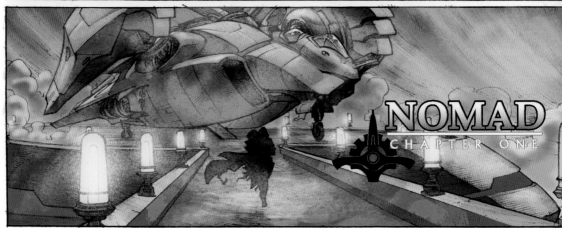

NOMAD
CHAPTER ONE

YOU KNOW HOW TO MAKE AN IMPRESSION, I'LL GIVE YOU THAT. YOU WERE HERE, HOW LONG? A COUPLE OF MINUTES?

NOW ONE OF MY BEST MEN WON'T EVER PLAY THE FANFAR AGAIN.

HE DIDN'T STRIKE ME AS A LOVER OF THE ARTS.

WELL, I GUESS NOW WE'LL NEVER KNOW.

HE WAS HOLDING A *GUN* TO A YOUNG BOY'S HEAD.

BUT DO YOU THINK TO ASK *WHY* HE'S HOLDING THE GUN TO THE BOY'S HEAD? NO, YOU JUST *ASSUME* THAT AN ADULT HOLDING A GUN TO A CHILD'S HEAD IS *WRONG*. PREJUDICE...

WHAT'S YOUR POINT?

MY *POINT* IS THIS IS *MY* OPERATION. THERE'S NO *LAWS* HERE, APART FROM THOSE *I* CHOOSE.

AND NOW I HAVE TO *CHOOSE* WHAT TO DO WITH YOU!

HMMM... A JEDI.

LOOK, YOU DON'T KNOW THE WHOLE STORY. LET ME GIVE YOU THE GUIDED TOUR, AND I'LL EXPLAIN WHAT YOU JUMPED INTO.

MAYBE YOU CAN HELP ME. I'M SAMUEL, BY THE WAY.

I'VE MET MEN LIKE YOU BEFORE, SAMUEL.

MEANING...?

I'D BE HAPPY TO TAKE YOUR TOUR.

BUT THE BOY COMES WITH US.

LEDDAR WAS GRABBED TWO DAYS AGO. HE WAS WITH HER AT THE TIME.

HE'S BEEN ON THE RUN EVER SINCE, RATHER THAN COME AND TELL ME WHAT HE KNOWS. THAT IMPLIES GUILT.

I DIDN'T DO ANYTHING. I WAS SCARED OF WHAT YOU'D DO TO ME. I WAS JUST WITH HER WHEN THE MAN GRABBED...

HOW OLD IS LEDDAR?

TWELVE.

SHE'S ELEVEN. WILL YOU BRING HER BACK?

I'LL TRY.

WHAT DO YOU WANT ME TO DO?

THE MAN WHO HAS LEDDAR IS A TRAINED MERCENARY. A KILLER. I HAVE THE MONEY, BUT I NEED SOMEONE TO DELIVER IT. SOMEONE WHO CAN MAKE SURE THE SCUM HONORS HIS AGREEMENT.

WHAT'S IN IT FOR ME?

I WASN'T AWARE THAT JEDI LOOKED FOR MONETARY GAIN.

I DON'T WANT YOUR MONEY, SAMUEL.

THEN WHAT DO YOU WANT?

I'M LOOKING FOR SOMEONE.

YOU'RE MOCKING ME? YOU THINK I DON'T HAVE JEDI MOVES? OH... NOW YOU'RE IN TROUBLE... OH, MAN...GET READY... I'LL SHOW YOU...

PZZZTTT

"DON'T YOU WANT TO SEE A BRAND NEW WORLD?"

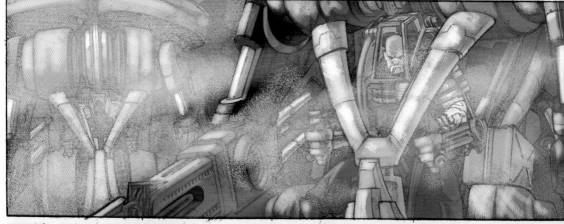

AND THIS PLACE WAS COMPLETELY DESERTED WHEN YOU FOUND IT?

YEAH, MAYBE THERE WERE PEOPLE ON THE PLANET MANY YEARS AGO, BUT NOTHING COULD LIVE HERE NOW.

GRENADE DISARM.

I DON'T WANT TO SEE THE GIRL HURT. JUST HIM-- AHH!

FZZZT!

YOU KIDNAP MY DAUGHTER? FIRE ROCKETS AT ME?

I'LL KILL YOU, ROYCE! YOU WON'T EVER GET YOUR --

UH...

VVVIIIIIIII!

WHATEVER HE TOLD YOU IS A LIE, JEDI. HE DOESN'T CARE ABOUT HIS DAUGHTER, YOU, OR ANYTHING ELSE. JUST HIS CREDITS.

DON'T LISTEN TO HIM. HE'S A LIAR AND A KIDNAPPER.

WHAT'S YOUR POINT?

SAMUEL AND I WERE PARTNERS. WE FOUND THIS PLANET TOGETHER, FOUND THE ORE. THEN HE SIGNED THE OWNERSHIP UP TO HIMSELF. CHEATED ME...

SO YOU KIDNAP HIS DAUGHTER? PUT HER IN HARM'S WAY?

LYCAN'S NEXT HEADING?

UH...A WORLD CALLED MOLAVAR ON THE SUPPLY ROUTE.

YOUR DAUGHTER'S SAFE, SAMUEL. YOU MAY NOT HAVE NOTICED. OUR DEAL'S OVER.

YOU'RE JUST GOING TO LEAVE THIS SLIME HERE?

I'M TAKING LEDDAR BACK WHERE IT'S SAFE AND WARM. YOU TWO CAN FIGHT IT OUT IF YOU LIKE.

LIVE A SHORT LIFE OF HATE AND REVENGE, IGNORE WHAT'S IMPORTANT...

I DON'T CARE.

ROYCE, YOU CAN KEEP THE LAND. LEDDAR... I'M SORRY...

NO...

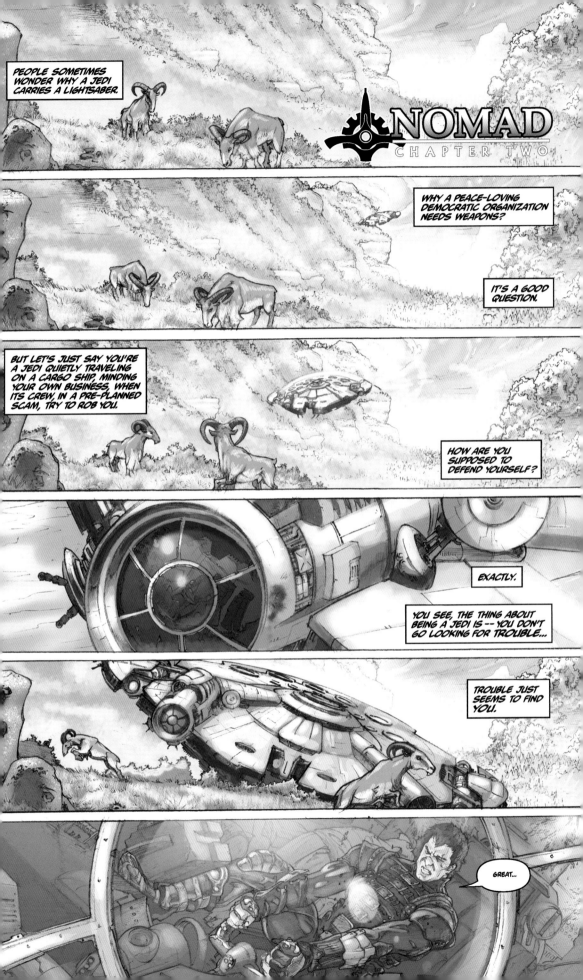

OKAY, SO IT TOOK 37 MINUTES.

GUESS THERE'S A REASON WHY I NEVER BECAME AN ENGINEER, EH?

BET THE CREW HAS PULLED THAT MOVE A HUNDRED TIMES BEFORE.

SOME LONE PASSENGER COMES ONBOARD ASKING FOR PASSAGE. THEY GET A FEW PARSECS INTO THE JOURNEY, THEN, WHAM. SEE YA.

I MEAN, THIS IS THE OUTER RIM. LOT OF BAD PEOPLE OUT HERE.

I LIKE THIS PLACE. NATURE'S EVERYWHERE.

COME ON... DON'T BE SHY. YOU WANT SOME?

IT HAS A KIND OF PEACE ABOUT IT.

HOAAARRR!!

I'LL TAKE THAT AS A YES.

I...FEEL AT HOME HERE. MAYBE I COULD BE HAPPY HERE...NO...

STUPID... STUPID MAN...

NOT WHILE HE'S STILL OUT THERE.

HER NAME IS JAREN, SHE TELLS ME LATER. SHE'S AN AMBASSADOR FROM A NEARBY COMMUNITY THAT'S HAD A LONGSTANDING DISPUTE WITH THE BIKER'S PEOPLE THAT WENT BACK CENTURIES.

HER BROTHER, AMENT, IS THE SLOW, LOYAL TYPE, APPARENTLY. SENT WITH HER FOR PROTECTION, ALTHOUGH A BLASTER IN THE BACK WILL SLOW DOWN THE BEST OF US.

THEY AGREED TO A SETTLEMENT AND THEN SENT THAT ASSASSIN AFTER US. IT SEEMS THEY DON'T WANT PEACE AFTER ALL.

I FEAR FOR MYSELF...AND FOR MY BROTHER, ALONE OUT HERE IN THE WILDERNESS. A JEDI PROTECTOR WOULD BE...WELCOME.

AND YOU COULD FIND A FREIGHTER AT OUR HOMETOWN THAT WILL TAKE YOU OFF-WORLD.

SHE'D BEEN SENT TO THE BIKER'S COUNTY TO NEGOTIATE SOME KIND OF PEACE SETTLEMENT.

SHE EXPLAINED MORE, BUT STRANGELY, I FOUND IT HARD TO CONCENTRATE...

EVEN IF IT IS SET ON STUN.

YES... UH... SORRY, I THINK I DRIFTED OFF FOR A SECOND.

THERE'S SOMETHING ABOUT THIS PLACE. MAYBE IT'S THE AIR. IT JUST SEEMS TO RELAX YOU.

IT'S THE PLANET. IT'S ALIVE, YOU KNOW.

UH... REALLY?

IT HAS A *TELEPATHIC* QUALITY. IT'S *EMOTIVE*. IT ENHANCES FEELINGS, READS PEOPLE. EMOTIONS AFFECT THE ELEMENTS HERE. LOOK--I'LL SHOW YOU AN EXAMPLE.

THIS IS A TRICK WE LEARN WHEN WE ARE CHILDREN.

WHAT ARE YOU DOING?

SHHH... YOU HAVE TO *CONCENTRATE*, EMPTY YOUR MIND.

YOU DON'T KNOW ME. THAT JUST HAPPENS NATURALLY.

QUIET.

OKAY... OKAY...

MY FIRST THOUGHT? HE DOESN'T STAND A CHANCE. THE THING'S TOO BIG, TOO FAST. IT'LL TEAR HIM TO SHREDS AND THEN TURN ON JAREN.

AND THEN I SEE HIS FEROCITY. HIS BILE AND HATRED FLOWING OUT.

THE CREATURE SEES IT, TOO. AND PANICS.

IT SEES HIS ROCK COMING DOWN WITH UNEARTHLY FURY AND INHUMAN REVULSION, AGAIN AND AGAIN...AND AGAIN.

AND IT REALIZES THAT IT IS DYING.

BUT AMENT DOES NOT STOP.

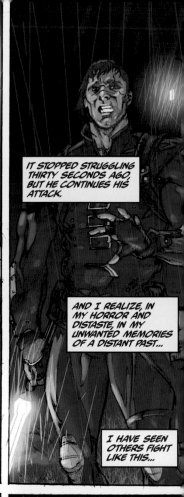

IT STOPPED STRUGGLING THIRTY SECONDS AGO, BUT HE CONTINUES HIS ATTACK.

AND I REALIZE, IN MY HORROR AND DISTASTE, IN MY UNWANTED MEMORIES OF A DISTANT PAST...

I HAVE SEEN OTHERS FIGHT LIKE THIS...

...THEY WERE MONSTERS, TOO...

...BROKEN...

YES.

HEY! UGLY SLEEPING MAN! HEY!

TOOTH-- YOU'RE A CHARMING INDIVIDUAL, AREN'T YOU?

WHAT DO YOU MEAN? YOU WAS SLEEPING. YOU IS UGLY. WHAT PROBLEM?

FAIR ENOUGH.

THERE THE SHIP YOU BEEN LOOKING FOR.

SCAVENGERS BEEN AT IT. IT LOOKS LIKE IT BEEN HERE A WEEK. MAYBE LESS.

KIND OF HARD TO MISS, ISN'T IT.

TOO HOT HERE. YOU STAY, YOU DIE. WE TRYING TO FIND SOMEWHERE TO SETTLE. SET UP FARMS. COME WITH US NOW, EH?

WHY WOULD HE LAND IT *HERE*? IT DOESN'T MAKE SENSE.

AH, YOU EVEN STUPIDER THAN YOU LOOK.

I GOT TO MOLAVAR FOUR DAYS AGO. THE PLACE WAS AWASH WIT TALES OF A MASS MURDER IN A CASINO, A MONSTER WHO COULD CONJURE DEATH FROM THIN AIR.

HE TOOK A SHIP. COULD'VE GONE ANYWHERE. FOR SOME REASON HE DIDN'T EVEN HIT LIGHT SPEED.

I MADE CONTACT WITH A FEW TRAFFIC CONTROLLERS ON NEARBY SYSTEMS. ASKED ABOUT ANYTHING STRANGE. TURNED OUT A SHIP HAD IGNORED DOCKING COMMANDS AND FLOWN OUT INTO THE DESERT.

CHECKED THE REGISTRATION AND WHAT D'YA KNOW...

THREE DAYS LATER.

YOU JUST STEPPED ON A MINE. IT'S OLD, BUT TRUST ME -- YOU DON'T WANT TO MOVE YOUR FOOT, UNLESS YOU'RE TIRED OF BEING A BIPED.

WHAT...?

CLICK!

WHAT DO YOU WANT ON MY LAND?

I DIDN'T *KNOW* IT WAS YOUR LAND.

NO ONE *SANE* WANDERS OUT HERE ALONE. YOUR WEAPONS, SHOW ME.

ONE BLASTER, DOESN'T WORK.

WE'LL SEE. WHAT'S THAT IN YOUR BELT?

LIGHTSABER.

LIGHT...

90

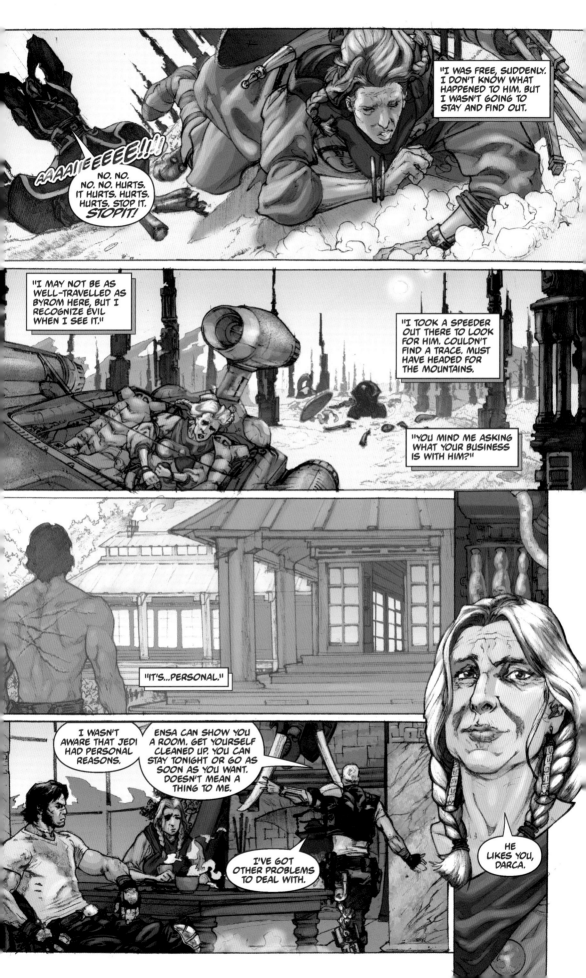

"SLEETH'S MOTHER, *MAGON*, IS A GANGSTER BOSS. RUNS ALL THE CRIME IN THE NEAREST TOWN, *MALCRAAN*. YOU CAME FROM THERE.

"A YEAR AGO SHE BRANCHED OUT HER OPERATION. OFFERING PROTECTION RACKETS TO THE SURROUNDING MOISTURE FARMS."

SHE HAS A SMALL ARMY AT HER DISPOSAL.

HOW MANY?

MORE THAN I CAN FIGHT, EVEN IF I WANTED TO. REGARDLESS OF MY...SKILLS.

IF YOU WANTED TO? THEY'RE THREATENING YOUR HOME. YOUR WIFE.

I'VE SEEN ENOUGH KILLING IN MY LIFE. I'VE DONE ENOUGH KILLING.

I FOUGHT SO MANY WARS I CAN'T EVEN NAME THEM ALL. EVENTUALLY I COULDN'T EVEN REMEMBER WHY I WAS FIGHTING IN THE FIRST PLACE.

YOU SPILL BLOOD AND IT DOESN'T JUST STOP. IT KEEPS ON RUNNING.

RIGHT AND WRONG? REVENGE? DEFENSE? GREED? I'VE HEARD ALL THE ARGUMENTS.

BUT YOU TAKE AWAY A MAN'S FUTURE AND PAST. ALL HE'S DONE AND COULD BE. *NOTHING* JUSTIFIES THAT. TOOK ME A LONG TIME TO REALIZE THAT...

IF THEY COME, IF THEY TRY TO TAKE ENSA, WHAT WILL YOU DO THEN?

WE'LL DEFEND OURSELVES.

WE CAME HERE TO *AVOID* BLOODSHED, DARCA. TO LIVE A DIFFERENT LIFE.

ENSA, BYROM, I'M SORRY. I WAS JUST TRYING TO...

I LEAVE AT DAWN, HEADING OUT FOR THE MOUNTAINS. THEY OFFER ME FOOD, UNDERSTANDING AND WARMTH.

I GO A HALF-MILE BEFORE I CAN BRING MYSELF TO LOOK BACK. I THINK I SEE THEM HUGGING.

IT'S COME TO THIS?

I LEAVE TWO GOOD PEOPLE TO DIE? TWO PEOPLE I COULD STILL HELP.

I DON'T DESERVE IT.

MAKING THE MOST OF THEIR FINAL PRIVATE MOMENTS.

TWO MORE LIVES ON MY CONSCIENCE.

FORGET THEM... CONCENTRATE... REMEMBER.

REMEMBER THE SMELLS OF THAT NIGHT...THE SOUNDS. REMEMBER HOW IT FELT.

YOU'RE SO CLOSE NOW. SO CLOSE TO ENDING IT.

BYROM AND ENSA COULD HELP THEM SET UP A FARM ON THEIR BORDERS. TOOTH'S PEOPLE COULD DEFEND THEM FROM MAGON AND MORE.

I LOVE HAPPY ENDINGS, BUT...

DROP GUNS AND RUN AWAY NOW PLEASE, REPULSIVE OILY CREATURE.

WE DEFEND THIS PLACE, YOU UNDERSTAND? NO ONE HURTS OUR NEW NEIGHBORS.

YOU HEARD HIM. MOVE ON.

...CATCHING UP WITH TOOTH'S CONVOY PUT ME ANOTHER WEEK BEHIND LYCAN.

YOU CAME BACK.

YES.

YOU SEE? PERHAPS YOU'RE NOT BEYOND SAVING, AFTER ALL.

MAGON WASN'T STUPID. SHE KNEW WHEN SHE WAS BADLY OUTGUNNED, SO OFF SHE RAN TO FIGHT ANOTHER DAY. MAYBE.

IT WAS THE PERFECT DEAL. TOOTH'S PEOPLE WERE LOOKING FOR SOMEWHERE TO SETTLE.

"PERHAPS. PERHAPS NOT."

WE'LL FIND OUT.

END OF CHAPTER THREE

NO.

YOU'RE NOT GOING TO BEAT HIM WITH A BLASTER.

THINK, YOU NEED A PLAN. YES...

GOOD...THAT'S GOOD, DARCA.

YOU DID GOOD.

I DOUBLE MY SPEED. EVENTUALLY GETTING A GOOD FEW HOURS AHEAD OF HIM. LOOKING... LOOKING FOR SOMETHING.

THE PERFECT SPOT.

THEN, MY WORK DONE, ALL THERE IS LEFT TO DO...IS WAIT.

AND IT'S STRANGE, BUT IN THIS MOMENT THAT SHOULD BE FILLED WITH TENSION, ANGER, AND EXCITEMENT...

SOMEHOW I DRIFT OFF...

...AND I REMEMBER.

LIVE A SHORT LIFE OF HATE AND REVENGE, IGNORE WHAT'S IMPORTANT...

I DON'T CARE.

NNN...

YOU ARE ILL INSIDE. I SEE THAT.

YOU HAVE DONE WRONG. YOU ARE BROKEN.

YOU REMIND ME OF HIM, A LONG TIME AGO. ANGRY. GUILTY. STRUGGLING WITH YOURSELF. YOU CARRY IT SO LONG, IT TURNS YOU INTO WHATEVER YOU'RE CHASING.

YOU CAN LET IT ALL GO, DARCA.

...LET IT GO...

"...YOU MUST...STOP HIM.

"HE IS A KILLER. HE IS...HE IS WITHOUT MERCY.

"TAKE THIS. IT IS MY... MY *LIGHTSABER!*"

IT MAY HELP YOU. YOU CAN STOP HIM.

I DON'T...

GO NOW!

"GO TO YOUR SON!"

"HE WAS ALL I HAD LEFT...

"HE WAS MY BOY.

"LYCAN"? YES...YES! I REMEMBER NOW.

I AM LYCAN. THEY WERE TAKING ME BACK TO CORUSCANT.

...YES...

"IT TOOK ME TWO DAYS TO BURY HIM AND TO BURN DOWN A LIFE THAT NO LONGER EXISTED.

"THEN I PACKED UP ALL I NEEDED AND FOLLOWED YOU."

I AM LYCAN, AND I AM FREE!

BUT, BEFORE I GO, I MUST THANK YOU.

WITHOUT YOU AND YOUR QUEST, I MAY NEVER HAVE REMEMBERED MYSELF.

NO, YOU'VE KILLED TOO MANY PEOPLE, NEAS. THOSE ON MOLOVAR. COUNTLESS OTHERS IN THE PAST. YOU'RE TOO DANGEROUS.

I CAN'T LET YOU LEAVE THIS CAVE ALIVE.

I THINK, IN YOUR PAIN, YOU HAVE MISREAD THE SITUATION. YOU ARE NOT THE VICTOR.

SOMETHING HAPPENED TO ME THE DAY NEAS DIED...

...THE DAY I PICKED UP THAT LIGHTSABER.

WAS IT THE FORCE?

NO, I HAVE NEVER FELT SUCH A THING.

WHEN MY JOURNEY BEGAN, I WANTED ONLY BLOODSHED, BUT ALONG THE WAY, WHEN PEOPLE SAW ME, THEY ASSUMED I WAS A JEDI.

AND THEY NEEDED MY HELP.

AND...I GAVE IT. I GAVE MYSELF.

IT WAS RIGHT. IT FELT GOOD.

IT WAS THE ONLY GOOD THING I'D FELT IN SO LONG.

AND NOW, TERIL AND NEAS, MY DARLINGS. TO MY SURPRISE...

...IN WHAT SHOULD BE MY FINAL, DARK MOMENTS...

...I SEE MY PATH BEFORE ME.

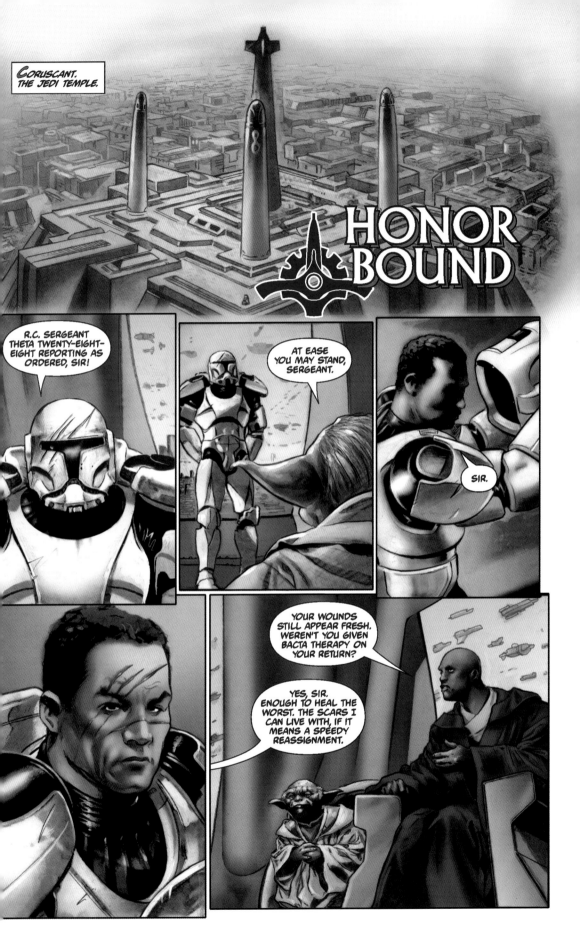

CORUSCANT.
THE JEDI TEMPLE.

HONOR BOUND

R.C. SERGEANT THETA TWENTY-EIGHT-EIGHT REPORTING AS ORDERED, SIR!

AT EASE YOU MAY STAND, SERGEANT.

SIR.

YOUR WOUNDS STILL APPEAR FRESH. WEREN'T YOU GIVEN BACTA THERAPY ON YOUR RETURN?

YES, SIR. ENOUGH TO HEAL THE WORST. THE SCARS I CAN LIVE WITH, IF IT MEANS A SPEEDY REASSIGNMENT.

HMMM. READ YOUR REPORT CONCERNING THE ACTION ON ASTURIAS WE HAVE. MOST INTRIGUING IT IS...MOST INTRIGUING INDEED.

SIR?

WE DO NOT QUESTION ITS VALIDITY. HOWEVER, WE WISH YOU TO CLARIFY CERTAIN POINTS FOR US -- COMMENCING WITH YOUR RETURN FROM THE CONFERENCE ON AVILES PRIME.

YES, SIR.

TWO DAYS AGO, WE WERE RUNNING ESCORT COVER FOR DIRECTOR OVIEDO AND HIS PARTY WHEN THEY REPORTED A MALFUNCTION IN THEIR LIFE-SUPPORT GENERATOR.

IN ORDER TO AFFECT REPAIRS, WE'D DROPPED OUT OF LIGHT-SPEED CLOSE TO THE DERELICT FACTORY MOON OF ASTURIAS.

WE'D DECELERATED FOR ORBITAL BREAKING -- WHEN AN UNDETECTED SEPARATIST DROID CONTROL SHIP FLANKED BY SEVERAL FIGHTER SQUADRONS CAME AT US.

OUR WING-MATE WAS DESTROYED INSTANTLY.

WE ENGAGED THE ENEMY, MANEUVERING BETWEEN THEM AND THE DIRECTOR'S VESSEL.

EVEN SO, THEY WERE HIT.

THE CAPTAIN ORDERED OUR PILOT TO FOLLOW THEM DOWN, SHIELDING THEM WITH OUR OWN SHIP, BUYING THEIR PILOT TIME TO MANAGE HIS DESCENT.

WE HELD FAST, BUT WERE NO MATCH FOR THEIR ORDNANCE.

EVENTUALLY, WE ALSO FELL...

BAMFF!

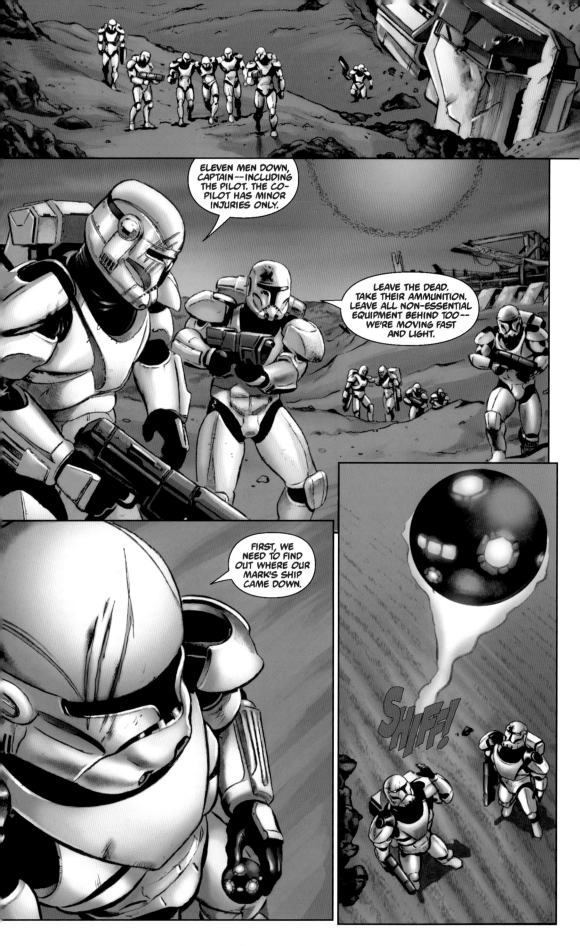

ELEVEN MEN DOWN, CAPTAIN--INCLUDING THE PILOT. THE CO-PILOT HAS MINOR INJURIES ONLY.

LEAVE THE DEAD. TAKE THEIR AMMUNITION. LEAVE ALL NON-ESSENTIAL EQUIPMENT BEHIND TOO-- WE'RE MOVING FAST AND LIGHT.

FIRST, WE NEED TO FIND OUT WHERE OUR MARK'S SHIP CAME DOWN.

SHIFF!

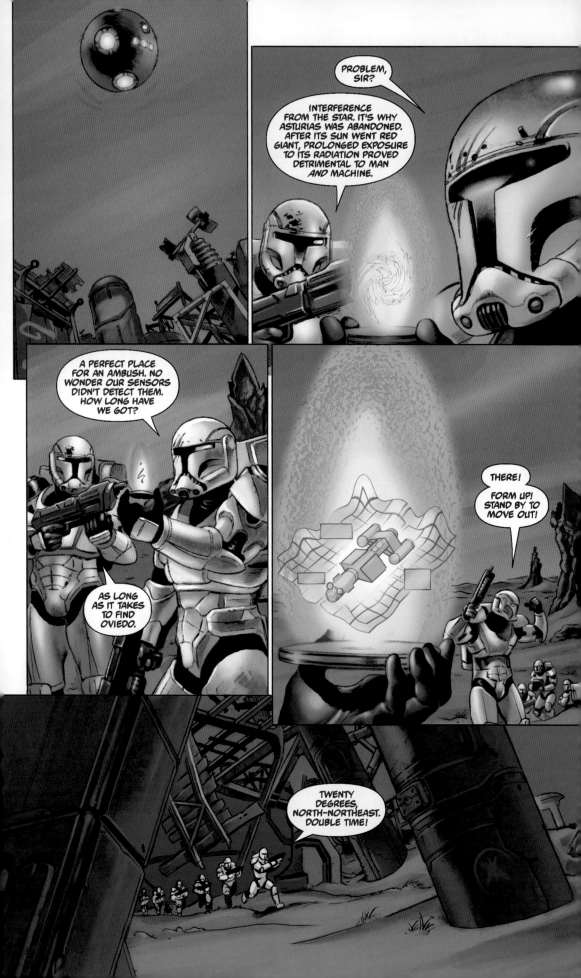

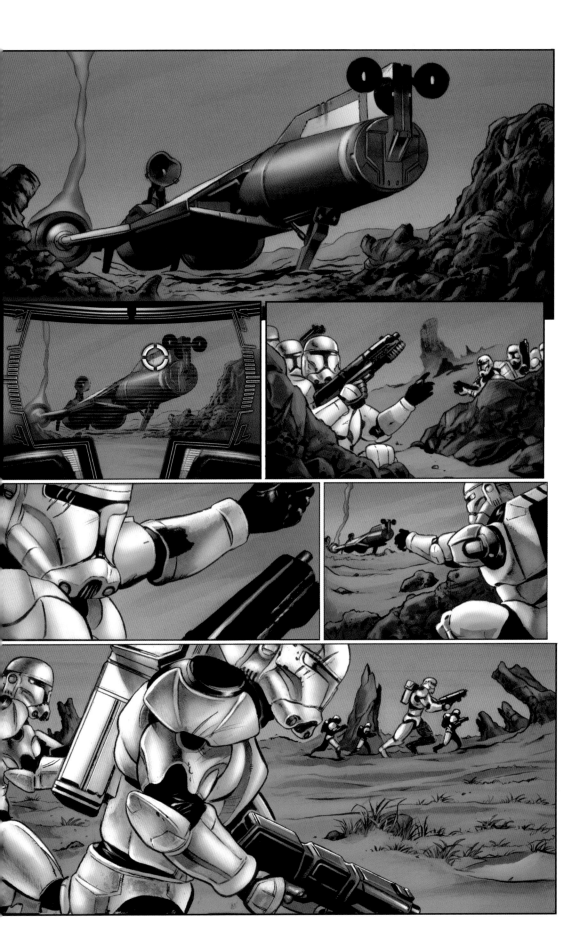

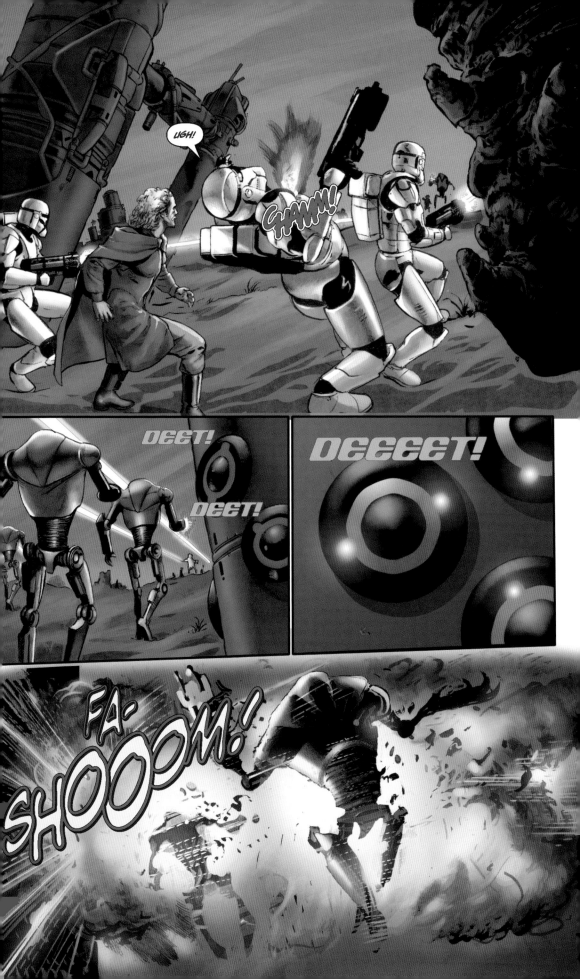

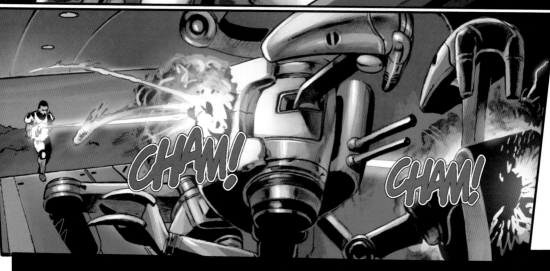

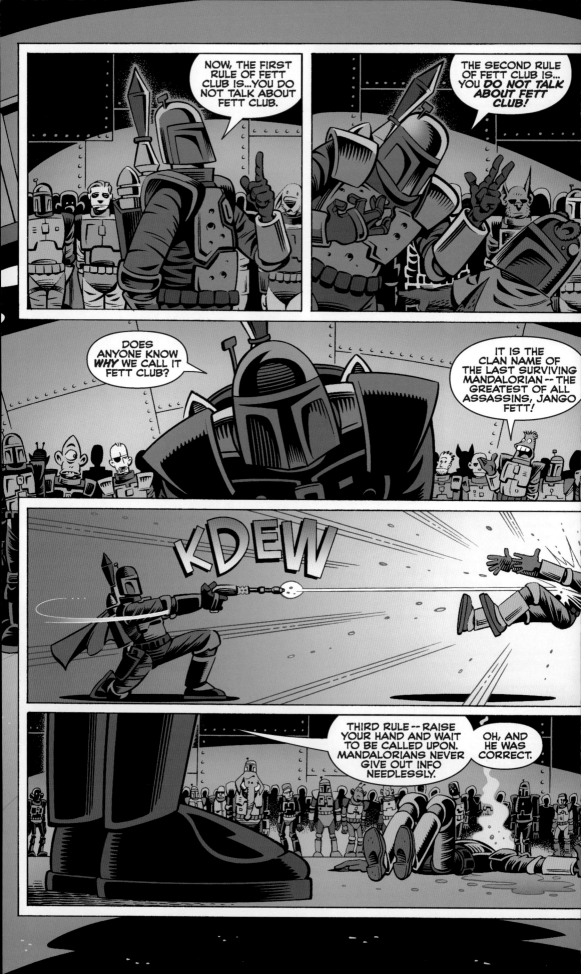

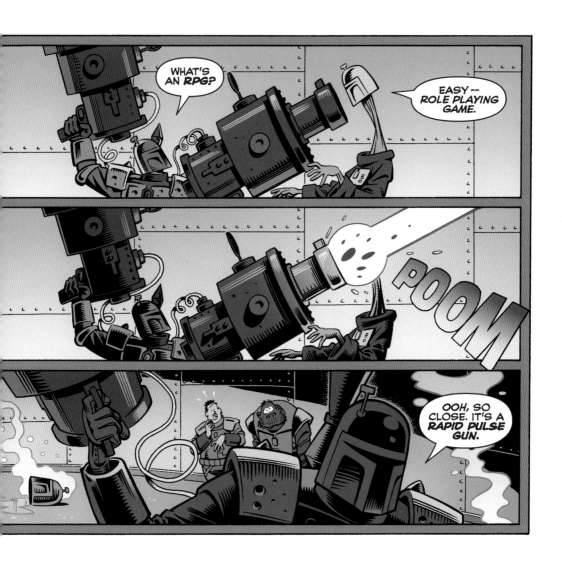

157

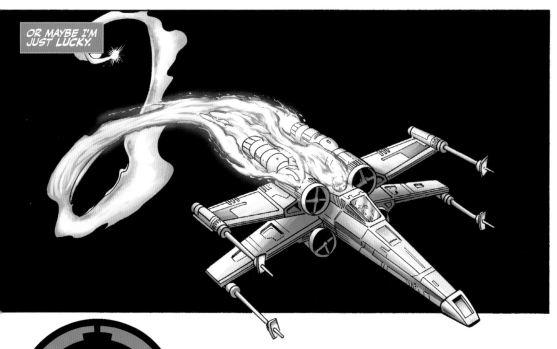

ROGUE LEADER? WEDGE?

I'VE GOT TWO ENGINES LEFT. HALF MY INSTRUMENTS ARE *GONE*.

WE JUST CLEANED UP THE LAST OF THOSE TIES, INCLUDING THE ONE THAT CLIPPED YOU.

WELL, THAT'S *ONE* BIT OF GOOD NEWS.

WEDGE!

AHH!!

FFZZZZ!!

I'M OKAY... CHECK MY LAST MESSAGE. NOW ALL MY INSTRUMENTS ARE GONE...

...ENGINES, TOO. I'M GOING DOWN. IT'S GOING TO BE A BUMPY LANDING.

NO ALTIMETER, SO I CAN'T TELL HOW HIGH I AM.

GO BY VISUAL.

IT'S PITCH *BLACK* OUT THERE. I CAN'T SEE A THING!

I COULD BE TWO HUNDRED METERS UP...OR TWO THOUSAND.

BLAST...

THERE COULD BE A MOUNTAIN RIGHT IN FRONT OF ME AND I WOULDN'T SEE IT.

AND IT REFLECTS FROM THE TINY CREATURES LIVING IN THE VAST LAKE BELOW.

WHETHER THEY'RE FISH, ALGAE OR SOMETHING ELSE, I DON'T KNOW.

AND THEN IT **HAPPENS.** JUST LIKE THAT. THE WIND PICKS UP, WEATHER PATTERNS CHANGE, LUCKY THINGS HAPPEN...WHATEVER. MOONLIGHT SHINES OUT.

NOR DO I CARE. I HAD A TARGET. A SOFT LANDING THAT WOULD PUT THE SHIP'S FIRE OUT.

IT COULDN'T HAVE WORKED OUT BETTER.

LUCKY?

MAYBE SO.

GUS TALON, CORELLIAN MOON. SIX YEARS EARLIER.

I'VE ALWAYS BEEN LUCKY.

ANTILLES!

UH-OH.

NO! NO! BREAKABLE! MY LIFE'S WORK! ALL VERY BREAKABLE! STOP!

SORRY!

NO!

NOT ONE...NOT ONE BROKEN.

THANK... THANK THE FORCE.

I AM BLESSED. TRULY.

TIK!

AAAHHH!

OOFF...

WEDGE!

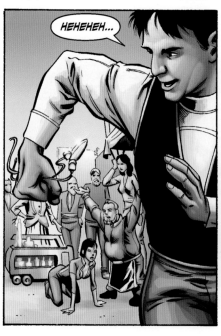

HEHEHEH...

STOP!

UH... LOOK OUT!

GOT YOU!

OOOFF...

OH, HI, RALLO. FANCY MEETING YOU HERE.

TELL THEM TO PUT THE GUNS DOWN -- HE'S JUST A BOY. HE MEANT NO HARM.

HE COULD HAVE BEEN A BOMBER, REBEL SCUM, ANYTHING.

AND HE LOOKS MORE LIKE A YOUNG MAN TO ME.

ENLISTMENT AGE, MAYBE?

CARE FOR A HEROIC CAREER SERVING OUR BELOVED EMPEROR? IN THE INFANTRY, PERHAPS?

I'M A PILOT.

HMMM...I DOUBT YOU HAVE WHAT IT TAKES TO FLY A TIE.

GET AWAY FROM HIM, TURRANT.

THAT'S CAPTAIN TURRANT.

WHEN ARE YOU AND YOUR TROOPS LEAVING?

OH, MAYBE IN A FEW WEEKS, MAYBE NEVER.

MAYBE A PERMANENT PRESENCE HERE IS WHAT YOU PEOPLE REALLY NEED...SOME GOOD, HEALTHY DISCIPLINE.

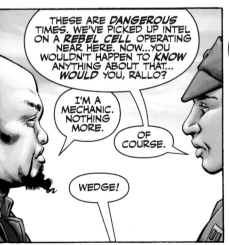

THESE ARE DANGEROUS TIMES. WE'VE PICKED UP INTEL ON A REBEL CELL OPERATING NEAR HERE. NOW...YOU WOULDN'T HAPPEN TO KNOW ANYTHING ABOUT THAT... WOULD YOU, RALLO?

I'M A MECHANIC. NOTHING MORE.

OF COURSE.

WEDGE!

I TOLD YOU I'D CATCH YOU. NOW, GIVE IT BACK AND KISS ME YOU BIG CORELLIAN GUNDARK!

I... OH... UM...HI DAD.

HELLO, MALA.

IT'S ONLY A MATTER OF TIME BEFORE YOUR FATHER *KILLS* ME -- YOU KNOW THAT, *RIGHT?*

HE *LIKES* YOU. WHY DO YOU THINK HE HELPS YOU WITH THE SHIP?

I GUESS... WHY DOES THE ENGINE TEMPERATURE KEEP ROCKETING?

YOU'VE GOT THE COOLANT ATTACHED TO THE MINOR VALVE INSTEAD OF THE MAJOR.

OH... THANKS.

I CAN'T *BELIEVE* I GOT THIS JOB TAKING MACHINE PARTS OFF-SYSTEM. IT'S BEEN *WEEKS* SINCE MY LAST *PAY-PACKET.*

I THOUGHT I WAS GOING TO HAVE TO SELL THE SHIP. IT COULDN'T HAVE COME AT A BETTER TIME.

LUCKY BOY.

I'LL BE GONE A DAY OR TWO. YOU OKAY WITH THAT?

WEDGE...WHEN YOU COME BACK, WILL YOU THINK ABOUT HELPING DAD? THE REBELLION COULD REALLY USE YOU AND YOUR SHIP.

I ADMIRE WHAT YOUR FATHER IS DOING. I DO. BUT...

YOU JUST DON'T SEE WHAT IT HAS TO DO WITH YOU...

EXACTLY. I DON'T WANT THE EMPIRE HERE EITHER, BUT THEY'RE NOT *MONSTERS.*

I'M GOING TO HELP HIM, WEDGE. I NEED TO DO *SOMETHING.*

OKAY, I'LL THINK ABOUT IT... WE'LL TALK WHEN I GET BACK, OKAY?

TWO DAYS?

TOPS.

FOR YOU, I'LL FLY LIKE THE *WIND.*

OOH. CHEESY.

"I LOVE YOU."

I DIDN'T SAY IT. I WANTED TO. WE WANTED TO.

IT'S WRONG THAT THESE MOMENTS PASS YOU BY, WITH NO WARNING.

THERE SHOULD BE A FEELING AT THE TIME... SOME KIND OF SIGN. SOMETHING THAT *STOPS* YOU...

...THAT MAKES YOU REALIZE YOU'LL NEVER GET THE CHANCE AGAIN.

RALLO!

WHAT DO YOU WANT, TURRANT? I'M WORKING!

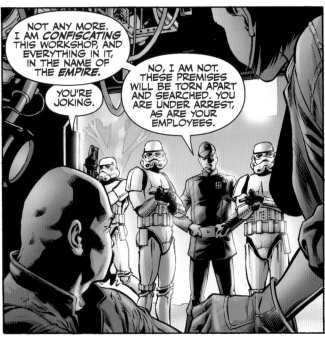

NOT ANY MORE. I AM *CONFISCATING* THIS WORKSHOP, AND EVERYTHING IN IT, IN THE NAME OF THE *EMPIRE*.

YOU'RE JOKING.

NO, I AM NOT. THESE PREMISES WILL BE TORN APART AND SEARCHED. YOU ARE UNDER ARREST, AS ARE YOUR EMPLOYEES.

DAD?

GO TO THE HOUSE, MALA. *NOW.*

DON'T MOVE, GIRL. YOU'RE ALSO UNDER ARREST.

ON WHAT CHARGE?

COLLUSION WITH THE REBELLION.

I'M SURE WE CAN FIND A NICE, COMFY CELL FOR HER, RALLO. SOMEWHERE OFF-WORLD AND FAR AWAY FROM YOUR PROTECTION. I'LL *ENJOY* THAT.

RUN, MALA!

KDEW!

KDEW!

KDEW!

I HEARD LATER THAT RALLO AND HIS MEN KILLED THE STORMTROOPERS...THE MEN THAT CAME TO TAKE HIS DAUGHTER AWAY.

A HEROIC STAND AGAINST AN OPPRESSIVE OCCUPYING FORCE, IT WAS SAID.

A BATTLE I'D HAVE BEEN PART OF, HAD I BEEN THERE.

THERE WERE BOUND TO BE REPURCUSSIONS. RALLO KNEW THAT.

THE EMPIRE WOULDN'T LET SUCH AN OPEN ACT OF INSURGENCE GO UNPUNISHED. A MESSAGE HAD TO BE DELIVERED.

MAYBE A FULL-SCALE INVASION OF THE SETTLEMENT...

...MAYBE SOMETHING WORSE.

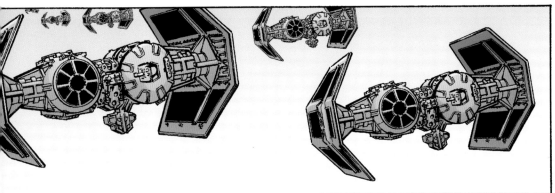

HE COULDN'T POSSIBLY HAVE IMAGINED.

GUS TALON STATION, DO YOU COPY? LOOKING FOR A DOCKING APPROACH HERE.

BY ORDER OF THE EMPEROR, GUS TALON IS NOW UNDER IMPERIAL RULE. ANY ATTEMPT TO ENTER THE SYSTEM WILL BE MET WITH DEADLY FORCE.

WHAT?

BUT...I LIVE THERE! YOU CAN'T...

REPEAT. TURN BACK NOW OR YOU WILL BE DESTROYED.

ALL CITIZENS OF GUS TALON ARE NOW PRISONERS OF THE EMPIRE.

MALA...

I COULDN'T TURN AWAY AND LEAVE HER. I HAD TO TRY.

I WAS LOST. NOT THINKING STRAIGHT. I DIDN'T KNOW WHAT TO DO.

THE REST IS JUST A BLUR.

I'M NOT EVEN SURE I REMEMBER FIRING THE BLASTERS.

I DIDN'T WANT TO RUN, BUT THERE WERE TOO MANY OF THEM.

AT THAT MOMENT I WANTED TO FIGHT THE EMPIRE. THE ENTIRE EMPIRE.

I WANTED TO LAND. I WANTED TO SEARCH FOR MALA. I WANTED TO FIND HER, HOLD HER, AND TELL HER EVERYTHING WAS OKAY.

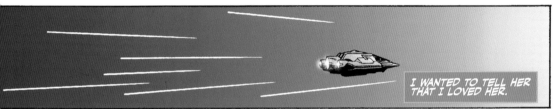

I WANTED TO TELL HER THAT I LOVED HER.

IT TOOK ME NINE DAYS TO GET INTO GUS TALON. SECURITY WAS TIGHT UP UNTIL THEN. DAY EIGHT WAS WHEN THE EMPIRE PULLED OUT.

YOU CAN'T BLAME THEM, AFTER ALL...

...THERE WASN'T MUCH LEFT TO GUARD. OR INVESTIGATE. OR DESTROY.

THERE WASN'T MUCH LEFT OF ANYTHING.

THE SURVIVORS TOLD ME THAT AFTER THE BOMBING, STORMTROOPERS CAME IN AND HAULED MOST PEOPLE OFF-WORLD ON PRISON SHIPS. NO ONE KNEW WHERE THEY WENT.

NO ONE KNEW IF MALA WAS WITH THEM.

IF I HADN'T TAKEN THAT JOB, I'D HAVE BEEN HERE. I'D HAVE BEEN KILLED OR IMPRISONED, TOO.

"LUCKY BOY."

EVERYONE IN THE REBELLION IS HERE FOR A *REASON*. EVERYONE WAS AFFECTED BY THE EMPIRE IN ONE WAY OR ANOTHER.

EVERYONE HAS A STORY TO TELL.

MOST OF THEM ARE TRAGIC.

I LOVE YOU, MALA.

LUCKY?

SOMETIMES IT DOESN'T FEEL LIKE IT.

END

THERE WAS A TIME WHEN HE WOULDN'T HAVE PUT UP WITH THIS.

A FLICK OF THE WRIST WOULD FLIP HIS SHIP -- THE RHODI'S SILENCE -- ON HER ENEMIES... A SLIGHT TWITCH OF HIS FINGER WOULD BLOW THEM OUT OF THE SKIES.

BUT THAT WAS A LONG TIME AGO, IN A PLACE THAT FEELS SO FAR AWAY...

WALKING THE PATH THAT'S GIVEN

...AND NAS GHENT IS NOT THE MAN HE USED TO BE.

FLYING ANOTHER IN A DREARY, ENDLESS STRING OF NEAR-SUICIDAL ASSIGNMENTS, HIS REFLEXES ARE AUTOMATIC.

THE OLD INSTINCTS GUIDE HIS HAND, SAVE HIS LIFE. KEEP HIM STANDING IN A FIGHT HE'S LONG SINCE GIVEN UP ON.

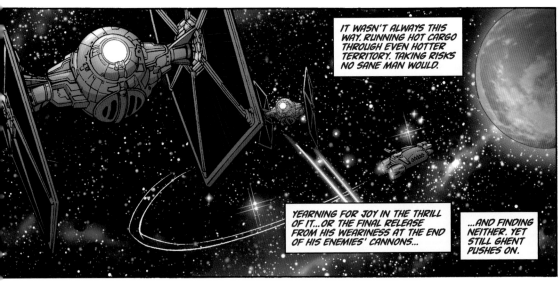

IT WASN'T ALWAYS THIS WAY. RUNNING HOT CARGO THROUGH EVEN HOTTER TERRITORY. TAKING RISKS NO SANE MAN WOULD.

YEARNING FOR JOY IN THE THRILL OF IT...OR THE FINAL RELEASE FROM HIS WEARINESS AT THE END OF HIS ENEMIES' CANNONS...

...AND FINDING NEITHER. YET STILL GHENT PUSHES ON.

AND THEN, THE UNTHINKABLE...

HE'D SPENT THE LAST THIRTY YEARS JOCKEYING FIGHTERS THROUGH IMPOSSIBLE ODDS, ALWAYS COMING OUT AHEAD, SOMETIMES ONLY JUST.

HE'D BEEN UNTOUCHABLE.

YET HERE IT WAS AND ALL OF THAT MEANT NOTHING NOW.

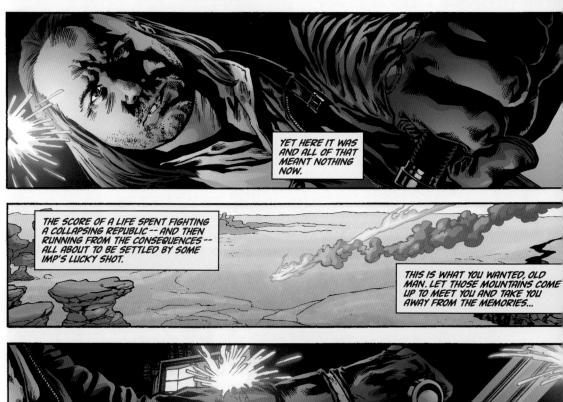

THE SCORE OF A LIFE SPENT FIGHTING A COLLAPSING REPUBLIC -- AND THEN RUNNING FROM THE CONSEQUENCES -- ALL ABOUT TO BE SETTLED BY SOME IMP'S LUCKY SHOT.

THIS IS WHAT YOU WANTED, OLD MAN. LET THOSE MOUNTAINS COME UP TO MEET YOU AND TAKE YOU AWAY FROM THE MEMORIES...

IF ONLY IT WERE THAT EASY...

AND ANOTHER REGRET IS ADDED TO AN ALREADY LONG LIST.

WHILE MOST MEN FEAR DYING, GHENT'S HORROR WAS THAT HE STILL LIVED. ONCE AGAIN A VICTIM OF HIS OWN SELF-PRESERVING STUBBORNNESS.

YOU...I SHOULD'A *KNOWN*...ONLY *YOU* COULD'A...LANDED A SHOT LIKE THAT.

I'VE BEEN *LOOKING* FOR YOU, NAS GHENT.

YOU'VE BEEN A THORN IN THE EMPIRE'S SIDE FOR TOO LONG.

NEVER FIGURED I RATED HIGH ENOUGH FOR THE EMPEROR TO NOTICE. I'M JUST A GUY MAKING A LIVING -- YOUR NO-FLY ZONES ALWAYS GOT IN THE WAY.

I DON'T HAVE ANY FIGHT LEFT -- LET'S GET THIS OVER WITH.

YOU HAVE MORE FIGHT LEFT THAN MOST MEN EVER POSSESS.

AND IT'S NOT THE EMPEROR'S ATTENTION YOU'VE EARNED -- IT'S MINE.

I'M NOT HERE TO KILL YOU, THOUGH I MIGHT... EVENTUALLY.

WHAT THEN?

YOUR SKILLS ARE IMPRESSIVE, BUT YOU WASTE THEM. I WANT YOU TO FLY FOR THE EMPEROR--FOR THE GLORY OF THE EMPIRE.

YOU HAVE YOUR PICK OF THE ACADEMY'S BEST. THAT FAILS, YOUR CLONERS CAN MIX YOU UP A PILOT.

WHY ME?

MY REASONS ARE OF NO CONCERN TO YOU.

I'M OFFERING YOU THAT FOR WHICH YOU'VE BEEN SEARCHING SINCE THE CLONE WARS ENDED -- A REASON TO LIVE OR A CHANCE TO DIE. AN ESCAPE FROM YOUR...REGRET.

WHAT DO *YOU* KNOW ABOUT REGRET?

SO THAT'S IT THEN. SIGN UP WITH YOU OR SIGN OFF OUT HERE IN THE MIDDLE OF NOWHERE.

KEEP TALKING.

A FEW DAYS LATER, IN ANOTHER REMOTE CORNER OF THE GALAXY...

DESPITE ITS IMPOSING MASS AND THE FORCEFUL ANGLES OF ITS STAGGERING, TRIANGULAR DESIGN, THERE'S NOTHING SPECIAL ABOUT THE STAR DESTROYER DESIGNATED CRUCIBLE.

IT'S JUST ANOTHER FACELESS SHIP IN THE EMPIRE'S VAST FLEET.

A COG IN THE MACHINE.

THE SAME COULD BE SAID ABOUT HER CREW.

THOUGH THERE ARE THOSE ABOARD WITH THE AMBITION TO BECOME *MORE* THAN THEIR STATION.

HOW DID HE GET PAST OUR ROLLING SECURITY CODES? WHERE IS HE NOW?

DORIN MILLAVEC IS SUCH A MAN.

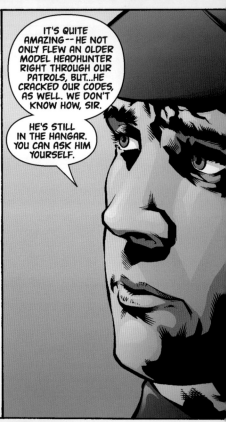

IT'S QUITE AMAZING -- HE NOT ONLY FLEW AN OLDER MODEL HEADHUNTER RIGHT THROUGH OUR PATROLS, BUT...HE CRACKED OUR CODES, AS WELL. WE DON'T KNOW HOW, SIR.

HE'S STILL IN THE HANGAR. YOU CAN ASK HIM YOURSELF.

I'LL DO MORE THAN *THAT.*

I WON'T BE MADE A *FOOL* OF, RESJIC. NOT WITH THE MOFF ONBOARD AND NOT WHEN I'M *SO CLOSE* TO BEIN' *PROMOTED* OUT OF HERE.

IF THIS *DERELICT* WANTS TO TRY MY *PATIENCE...*

"...HE'S ABOUT TO LEARN A HARD LESSON."

SNEAKING THE OUTDATED SHIP IN UNDER THE EMPIRE'S RADAR SHOULD HAVE BEEN ENOUGH. IMPOSSIBLE ODDS. LITTLE CHANCE OF SURVIVAL. AN ADRENALINE JUNKIE'S DREAM.

DESPITE HIMSELF, GHENT CAN'T HELP BUT FEEL A SMALL SATISFACTION...

CONGRATULATIONS-- YOU SLIPPED THROUGH THE *CRACKS* IN OUR DEFENSES.

YOU AND YOUR *DIRTY LITTLE SHIP* HAVE SUCCEEDED WHERE NEWER CRAFTS AND BETTER PILOTS HAVE *FAILED*, AND I PROMISE YOU THAT MANY OF MY MEN WILL BE *DISCIPLINED* FOR LETTING IT HAPPEN.

I DON'T KNOW *WHO* SENT YOU OR *WHAT* YOU'RE TRYING TO ACCOMPLISH, BUT YOU'LL FIND *NO MERCY* HERE.

YOU CAN'T BE SERIOUS!

THIS IS UNORTHODOX, TO SAY THE LEAST, AND I CAN'T BE PARTY TO A PROGRAM THAT CIRCUMVENTS THE PROPER CHANNELS, OR ONE THAT COULD POTENTIALLY EMBARRASS THE EMPIRE!

ON WHOSE AUTHORIZATION--

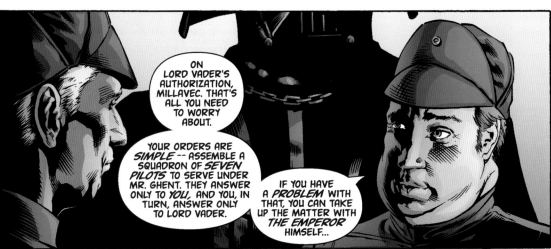

ON LORD VADER'S AUTHORIZATION, MILLAVEC. THAT'S ALL YOU NEED TO WORRY ABOUT.

YOUR ORDERS ARE *SIMPLE* -- ASSEMBLE A SQUADRON OF *SEVEN PILOTS* TO SERVE UNDER MR. GHENT. THEY ANSWER ONLY TO *YOU,* AND YOU, IN TURN, ANSWER ONLY TO LORD VADER.

IF YOU HAVE A *PROBLEM* WITH THAT, YOU CAN TAKE UP THE MATTER WITH *THE EMPEROR* HIMSELF...

THAT'S NOT WHAT I'M *SAYING,* GENERAL MAK, AND YOU *KNOW* IT.

BUT FORGIVE ME IF I FAIL TO SEE THE WISDOM IN TURNING A SQUADRON OF MY BEST PILOTS OVER TO...

...THAT!

IT SURPRISED HIM HOW LITTLE HAD CHANGED.

SMALL MEN IN POWER ARGUING OVER SMALL THINGS. PROCEDURE. REGULATIONS.

HOW BEST TO SEND THEIR BOYS TO THEIR DEATHS.

HE'D LAUGH, IF HE COULD.

BESIDES, I'M NOT YOUR MAN. I'M TO BE PROMOTED OUT OF THE FLIGHT DECK AND INTO LOWER COMMAND. YOU'LL HAVE TO FIND ANOTHER--

YOU *WILL* COMPLETE THIS ASSIGNMENT AS INSTRUCTED, OR YOU'LL BE TRANSFERRED TO AN IMPERIAL LISTENING POST ON THE OUTER RIM, NEVER TO BE SEEN AGAIN.

THAT IS OF LITTLE IMPORTANCE TO ME.

Y-YES, OF COURSE, LORD VADER. I MEANT NO--

I'LL GET STARTED RIGHT AWAY.

AS I EXPECTED.

YOU'RE TO FIND A GROUP OF INDEPENDENT THINKERS WHO CAN OPERATE OUTSIDE OF THE EMPIRE'S BUREAUCRACY.

PULL THEM FROM THE IMPERIAL PRISON SYSTEM, IF YOU HAVE TO.

ONCE THE SQUAD IS FORMED, GHENT WILL TAKE OVER. HE KNOWS WHAT TO DO.

I EXPECT MY ORDERS TO BE FOLLOWED TO THE LETTER, COMMANDER MILLAVEC...

...I WILL NOT TOLERATE FAILURE.

I'M BEING SET UP, RESJIN. I CAN *FEEL* IT. I WAS *SO CLOSE*... BUT THEY *WANT* ME TO FAIL.

HOW AM I SUPPOSED TO *RESPOND* TO THAT?

YES, SIR.

DID YOU FIND THAT INFORMATION ON GHENT?

YES, SIR. YOU WOULDN'T KNOW IT TO LOOK AT HIM, BUT OUR GUY'S A FULL-FLEDGED WAR HERO.

HE FOUGHT IN THE CLONE WARS ON THE SEPARATISTS' SIDE. CAUSED THE REPUBLIC A LOT OF GRIEF.

"HE HAS ALMOST AS MANY MEDALS AS HE DOES CONFIRMED KILLS.

"HE WAS INVOLVED WITH SOME OF THE CONFEDERACY'S MOST DEVASTATING CAMPAIGNS, INCLUDING THE ASSAULT ON CORUSCANT.

"WE ALL KNOW HOW *THAT* ENDED.

"AFTER THAT, HE DISAPPEARS FOR OVER A *DECADE*, ONLY TO REAPPEAR SMUGGLING BACTA AND GLITTERYLL THROUGH SOME PRETTY HOSTILE SPACE.

"HE HAS A REPUTATION FOR PUTTING HIMSELF IN HARM'S WAY, OF TAKING UNNECESSARY RISKS...

"...OF BEING INSANE."

PERSONALLY, I THINK THAT'S WHAT HE *WANTS* US TO BELIEVE.

HE'S JUST A *MAN*, WHICH MEANS HE CAN BE *BROKEN* LIKE THE REST.

DON'T UNDERESTIMATE HIM, RESJIC. I'VE SEEN HIS TYPE BEFORE -- COMBAT-FATIGUED EX-SOLDIERS WITH NOWHERE TO GO ONCE THE WAR'S OVER.

IT'S A VERY *DANGEROUS* MIX. ONE THAT'S GOING TO MAKE OUR JOB THAT MUCH MORE DIFFICULT.

PERHAPS NOT, SIR...

"PERHAPS WE CAN USE THAT TO OUR ADVANTAGE.

"IF GHENT HAS A DEATH WISH...

THIS IS CONTROL -- YOU HEAR US IN THERE, GHENT?

AFFIRMATIVE, CONTROL -- LOUD AND CLEAR.

"...PERHAPS WE CAN OBLIGE HIM."

THIS IS GHENT -- FORM UP ON MY MARK.

YES...YES.

SEE THAT GHENT IS GIVEN ONE OF OUR *DECOMMISSIONED* TIES, PREFERABLY ONE *WITHOUT* WORKING BLASTER CANNONS -- THEN TELL YOUR MEN TO FLY *MANEUVER 717.*

IN THE *MEANTIME*, I'LL WORK ON THAT *PILOTS* LIST, JUST IN CASE.

ROGER THAT, SIR. ORDER RELAYED.

YOU EVER HEARD OF MANEUVER 717 BEFORE?

OH YEAH -- IT'S WHAT YOU DO YOU WHEN YOU FIND A SPY OR AN ENEMY AGENT IN YOUR FLIGHT GROUP, ONLY THEY DON'T KNOW YOU'RE ON TO THEM.

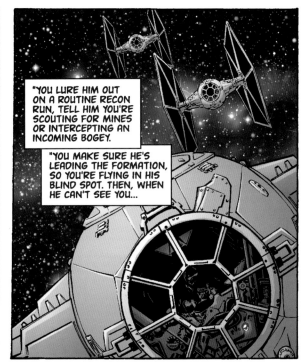

"YOU LURE HIM OUT ON A ROUTINE RECON RUN, TELL HIM YOU'RE SCOUTING FOR MINES OR INTERCEPTING AN INCOMING BOGEY.

"YOU MAKE SURE HE'S LEADING THE FORMATION, SO YOU'RE FLYING IN HIS BLIND SPOT. THEN, WHEN HE CAN'T SEE YOU...

"...YOU BLAST HIM OUT OF THE SKY!"

ONCE *THAT'S* TAKEN CARE OF, WE'LL SET OUT TO FIND WHO PUT ME UP TO THIS INDIGNITY. SOMEONE AT THE TOP WANTS TO KEEP ME AT THE BOTTOM.

WHEN WE FIND OUT WHO THEY ARE...THERE'S GOING TO BE HELL TO PAY.

THIS CAN'T BE RIGHT...

COME TAKE A LOOK AT THIS.

WHAT THE--?!

WHERE ARE THE OTHER FIGHTERS?!

"HE TOOK THEM OUT!"

188

IF WE PLACE THEM HERE-- AND HERE...

LISTEN, YOU LITTLE SNAKE-- IF YOU'RE GOING TO PUT A KNIFE IN MY BACK, YOU'D BETTER BE MAN ENOUGH TO DO IT YOURSELF.

OR YOU'D BETTER BE READY TO DIE TRYING.

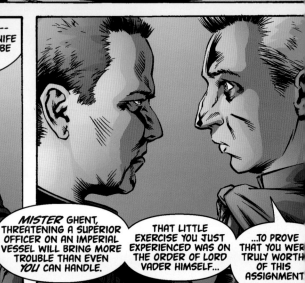

MISTER GHENT, THREATENING A SUPERIOR OFFICER ON AN IMPERIAL VESSEL WILL BRING MORE TROUBLE THAN EVEN YOU CAN HANDLE.

THAT LITTLE EXERCISE YOU JUST EXPERIENCED WAS ON THE ORDER OF LORD VADER HIMSELF...

...TO PROVE THAT YOU WER TRULY WORTH OF THIS ASSIGNMENT

YOU'VE MADE IT MORE THAN CLEAR THAT YOU ARE.

NOW IF I WERE YOU, I'D GO GET SOME REST. YOUR PILOT RECRUITMENT BEGINS TOMORROW, AND YOU'LL FIND RETRIEVING THESE CANDIDATES TO BE QUITE GRUELING.

WE'RE NOT SETTLED, MILLAVEC.

NOT BY A LONG SHOT.

WHAT ARE YOU GOING TO DO WHEN HE FINDS OUT IT *WASN'T* VADER WHO SET HIM UP?

THIS COULD BE A BIGGER PROBLEM THAN WE EXPECTED.

HARDLY. THIS LIST OF PILOTS I'VE ASSEMBLED? IT ISN'T COMPRISED OF THE BEST OR MOST AGREEABLE MEN THE EMPIRE'S HOLDING...

"...GHENT'S ABOUT TO FIND HIMSELF ALONE AND FACE-TO-FACE WITH THE MOST BRUTAL AND BLOODTHIRSTY CONVICTS EVER TO SERVE TIME.

"CUTTHROATS, MURDERERS, MADMEN...

"IT'S ONLY A MATTER OF TIME BEFORE OUR PROBLEMS ARE TAKEN CARE OF FOR US."

AND VADER?

HIS *OBSESSION* WITH FINDING THAT REBEL PILOT WHO DESTROYED THE DEATH STAR WILL KEEP HIM OCCUPIED...

"...BY THE TIME HE GETS AROUND TO CHECKING BACK IN ON US, GHENT WILL BE A SMEAR ON A PRISON WALL. A DISTANT MEMORY."

IF MILLAVEC ONLY KNEW WHAT HIS BETRAYAL HAS REALLY UNLEASHED.

FREED FROM THE REGRET AND LETHARGY THAT HELD HIM DOWN FOR SO LONG, GHENT IS NO LONGER THE LOST SOUL HE ONCE WAS.

VADER WAS *RIGHT* -- HIS DUTY *HAS* GIVEN HIS LIFE NEW PURPOSE.

HE'LL MOLD THIS SQUADRON --THIS *BLACK EIGHT*-- INTO THE MOST EFFICIENT AND TERRIFYING UNIT THE EMPIRE'S EVER SEEN.

AND IF COMMANDER MILLAVEC IS BROUGHT DOWN IN THE PROCESS...

...SO BE IT.

THE EN

MAROONED

TRUCE?

OKAY.

SO, THEY LEFT YOU BEHIND TOO, HUH?

THEY'LL BE BACK.

WHAT'RE YOU SAYING?

YOU DON'T KNOW? THE EMPEROR IS DEAD.

DON'T COUNT ON IT, EGG MAN.

THAT'S IMPOSSIBLE... HOW?

VELL...USING A STOLEN IMPERIAL SHUTTLE, WE INFILTRATED AND 'EACTIVATED THE DEATH STAR'S SHIELD GENERATOR HERE ON THE SURFACE.

MEANWHILE, THE ALLIANCE FLEET CREATED A PERIMETER WHILE A COUPLE OF FIGHTERS FLEW INTO THE DEATH STAR'S SUPERSTRUCTURE AND KNOCKED OUT ITS MAIN REACTOR CORE.

AND THAT WAS IT?

PRETTY MUCH, YES.

NOW I KNOW YOU'RE LYING -- THAT'S THE *DUMBEST* PLAN I EVER HEARD.

...OKAY, SO *NEITHER* OF US KNOW WHO ACTUALLY WON.

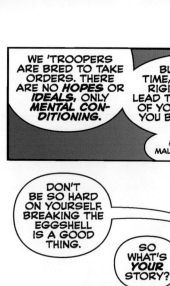

WE 'TROOPERS ARE BRED TO TAKE ORDERS. THERE ARE NO *HOPES* OR *IDEALS*, ONLY *MENTAL CONDITIONING.*

BUT WHEN, OVER TIME, YOU WATCH THAT RIGID CONDITIONING LEAD TO THE SLOW DEATH OF YOUR SQUAD-MATES, YOU BEGIN TO *RETHINK* THINGS.

MAYBE I'M MALFUNCTIONING.

DON'T BE SO HARD ON YOURSELF. BREAKING THE EGGSHELL IS A GOOD THING.

SO WHAT'S *YOUR* STORY?

I WAS WITH THE STRIKE TEAM, BUT WE GOT... SEPARATED.

WHEN YOU HAVE TO GO, YOU HAVE TO GO.

YOU'RE AN *IDIOT.*

ASK YOUR FRIENDS IF THEY KNOW WHERE *THIS* IS.

YUB?

YUB YUB!

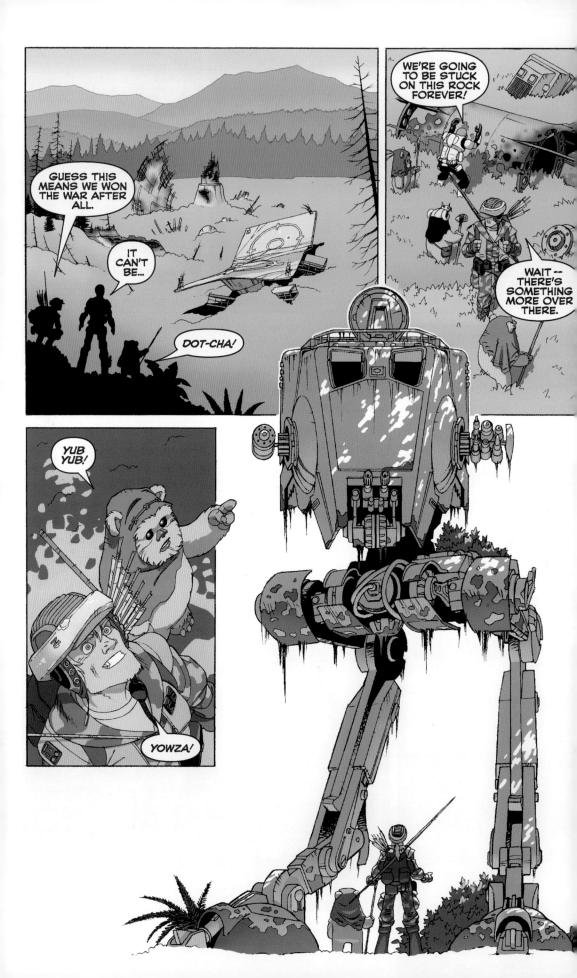

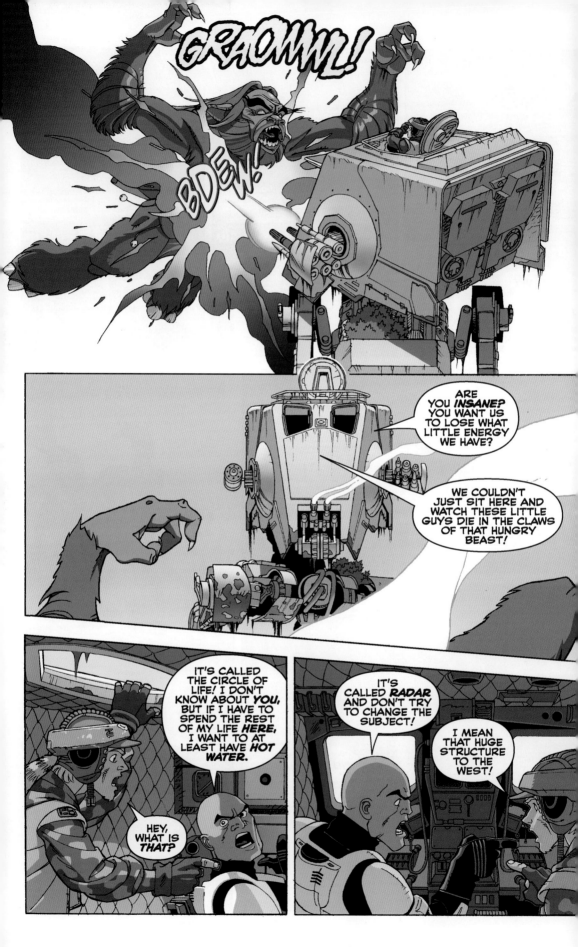

I DON'T KNOW. BUT IT'S THE SIZE OF A SMALL CITY.

IS IT IMPERIAL?

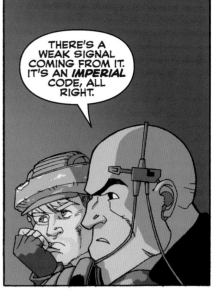
THERE'S A WEAK SIGNAL COMING FROM IT. IT'S AN *IMPERIAL* CODE, ALL RIGHT.

LOOK ON THE BRIGHT SIDE... THIS MEANS FINALLY GETTING OUT OF HERE.

HINK

K-CH

NK

K-CHINK

K-CH

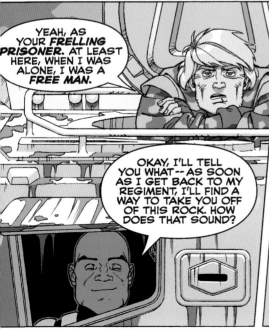
YEAH, AS YOUR *FRELLING PRISONER.* AT LEAST HERE, WHEN I WAS ALONE, I WAS A *FREE MAN.*

OKAY, I'LL TELL YOU WHAT -- AS SOON AS I GET BACK TO MY REGIMENT, I'LL FIND A WAY TO TAKE YOU OFF OF THIS ROCK. HOW DOES THAT SOUND?

HOLY HUTT!

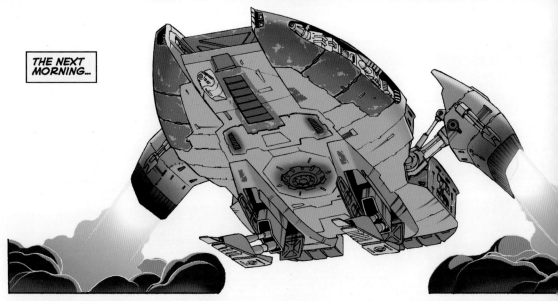

THE NEXT MORNING...

YOU *SURE* ABOUT THIS?

YOU WERE *RIGHT.* PEOPLE LIKE ME DON'T HAVE A PLACE IN PEACEFUL SOCIETY. AT LEAST *HERE* I HAVE A *CHOICE.*

MAYBE WHEN I'M READY.

TAKE YOUR TIME, PAL. AND IF YOU CHANGE YOUR MIND LET ME KNOW, OKAY?

SEE YOU AROUND, EGG MAN!

GET OUT OF HERE.

EN

THAT REALLY HUR-- UNGH!

BUT THEN...

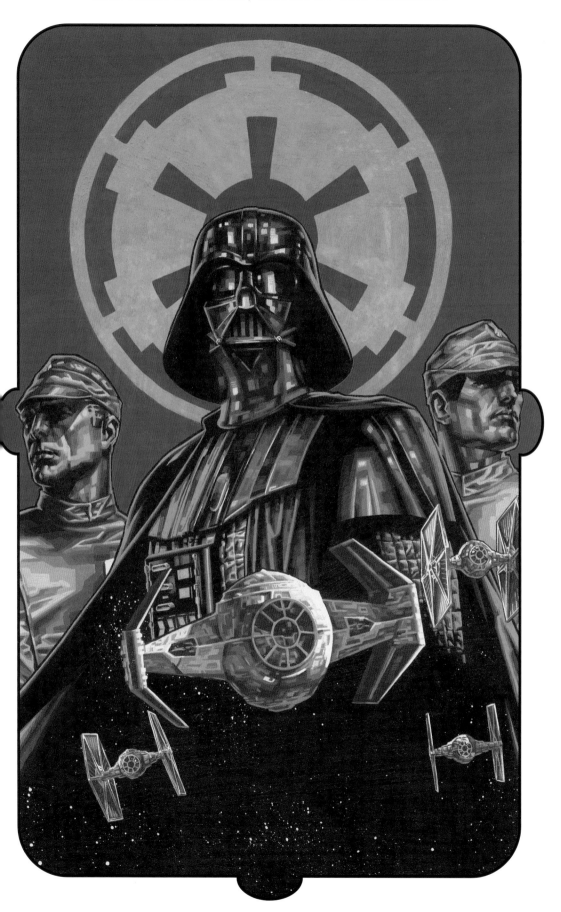

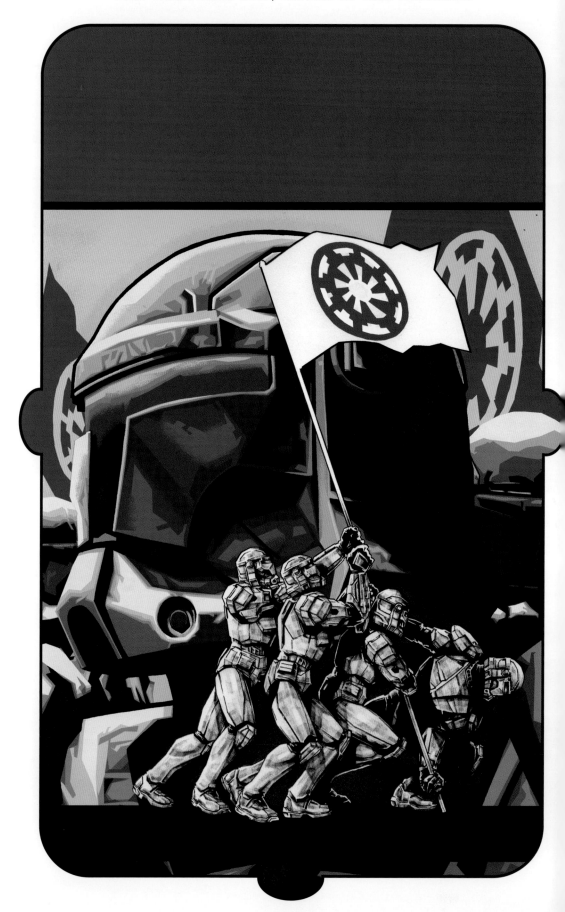

THE REAL LIFE STAR WARS TALES
ADVENTURES OF JEREMY BARLOW
Collecting the introduction pages from past issues of *Star Wars Tales*.

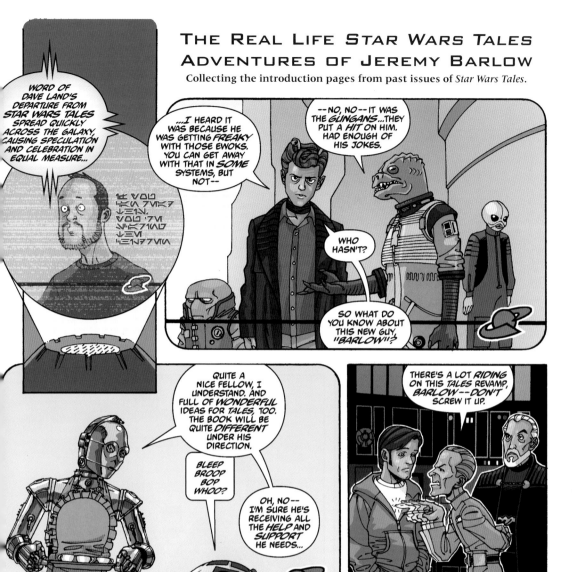

ISSUE TWENTY

Script / JEREMY BARLOW   Art / LUCAS MARANGON
Colors / JASON HVAM   Letters / MICHAEL HEISLER

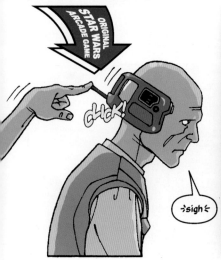

ISSUE TWENTY-ONE

Script / JEREMY BARLOW   Art / LUCAS MARANGON

Colors / JASON HVAM   Letters / MICHAEL HEISLER

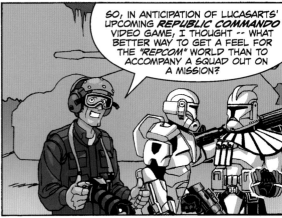

ISSUE TWENTY-TWO

Script / JEREMY BARLOW   Art / LUCAS MARANGON
Colors / JASON HVAM   Letters / MICHAEL HEISLER

ISSUE TWENTY-THREE
Script / JEREMY BARLOW   Art / LUCAS MARANGON
Colors / JASON HVAM   Letters / MICHAEL HEISLER

ISSUE TWENTY-FOUR

Script / JEREMY BARLOW   Art / LUCAS MARANGON
Colors / JASON HVAM   Letters / MICHAEL HEISLER

STAR WARS®

TIMELINE OF TRADE PAPERBACKS AND GRAPHIC NOVELS!

OLD REPUBLIC ERA:
25,000-1000 YEARS BEFORE
STAR WARS: A NEW HOPE

Tales of the Jedi—
Knights of the Old Republic
ISBN: 1-56971-020-1 $14.95

Dark Lords of the Sith
ISBN: 1-56971-095-3 $17.95

The Sith War
ISBN: 1-56971-173-9 $17.95

The Golden Age of the Sith
ISBN: 1-56971-229-8 $16.95

The Freedon Nadd Uprising
ISBN: 1-56971-307-3 $5.95

The Fall of the Sith Empire
ISBN: 1-56971-320-0 $15.95

Redemption
ISBN: 1-56971-535-1 $14.95

Jedi vs. Sith
ISBN: 1-56971-649-8 $17.95

RISE OF THE EMPIRE ERA:
1000-0 YEARS BEFORE
STAR WARS: A NEW HOPE

The Stark Hyperspace War
ISBN: 1-56971-985-3 $12.95

Prelude to Rebellion
ISBN: 1-56971-448-7 $14.95

Jedi Council—Acts of War
ISBN: 1-56971-539-4 $12.95

Darth Maul
ISBN: 1-56971-542-4 $12.95

Jedi Council—
Emissaries to Malastare
ISBN: 1-56971-545-9 $15.95

Episode I—
The Phantom Menace
ISBN: 1-56971-359-6 $12.95

Episode I—
The Phantom Menace Adventures
ISBN: 1-56971-443-6 $12.95

Outlander
ISBN: 1-56971-514-9 $14.95

Star Wars: Jango Fett—
Open Seasons
ISBN: 1-56971-671-4 $12.95

The Bounty Hunters
ISBN: 1-56971-467-3 $12.95

Twilight
ISBN: 1-56971-558-0 $12.95

The Hunt for Aurra Sing
ISBN: 1-56971-651-X $12.95

Darkness
ISBN: 1-56971-659-5 $12.95

The Rite of Passage
ISBN: 1-59307-042-X $12.95

Episode II—Attack of the Clones
ISBN: 1-56971-609-9 $17.95

Clone Wars Volume 1:
The Defense of Kamino
ISBN: 1-56971-962-4 $14.95

Clone Wars Volume 2:
Victories and Sacrifices
ISBN: 1-56971-969-1 $14.95

Clone Wars Adventures Volume 1
ISBN: 1-59307-243-0 $6.95

Clone Wars Volume 3:
Last Stand on Jabiim
ISBN: 1-59307-006-3 $14.95

Clone Wars Volume 4: Light and Dark
ISBN: 1-59307-195-7 $16.95

Droids—The Kalarba Adventures
ISBN: 1-56971-064-3 $17.95

Droids—Rebellion
ISBN: 1-56971-224-7 $14.95

Classic Star Wars—
Han Solo At Stars' End
ISBN: 1-56971-254-9 $6.95

Boba Fett—Enemy of The Empire
ISBN: 1-56971-407-X $12.95

Dark Forces—
Soldier for the Empire GSA
ISBN: 1-56971-348-0 $14.95

Mara Jade—By the Emperor's Hand
ISBN: 1-56971-401-0 $15.95

Underworld
ISBN: 1-56971-618-8 $15.95

Empire Volume 1: Betrayal
ISBN: 1-56971-964-0 $12.95

Empire Volume 2: Darklighter
ISBN: 1-56971-975-6 $17.95

REBELLION ERA:
0-5 YEARS AFTER
STAR WARS: A NEW HOPE

Classic Star Wars, Volume 1:
In Deadly Pursuit
ISBN: 1-56971-109-7 $16.95

Classic Star Wars, Volume 2:
The Rebel Storm
ISBN: 1-56971-106-2 $16.95

Classic Star Wars, Volume 3:
Escape to Hoth
ISBN: 1-56971-093-7 $16.9

Classic Star Wars—
The Early Adventures
ISBN: 1-56971-178-X $19.9

Jabba the Hutt—The Art of the Deal
ISBN: 1-56971-310-3 $9.9

Vader's Quest
ISBN: 1-56971-415-0 $11.9

Splinter of the Mind's Eye
ISBN: 1-56971-223-9 $14.9

A Long Time Ago... Volume 1:
Doomworld
ISBN: 1-56971-754-0 $29.9

A Long Time Ago... Volume 2:
Dark Encounters
ISBN: 1-56971-785-0 $29.9

A Long Time Ago... Volume 3:
Resurrection of Evil
ISBN: 1-56971-786-9 $29.9

A Long Time Ago... Volume 4:
Screams in the Void
ISBN: 1-56971-787-7 $29.95

A Long Time Ago... Volume 5:
Fool's Bounty
ISBN: 1-56971-906-3 $29.95

A Long Time Ago... Volume 6:
Wookiee World
ISBN: 1-56971-907-1 $29.95

A Long Time Ago... Volume 7:
Far, Far Away
ISBN: 1-56971-908-X $29.95

Battle of the Bounty Hunters
Pop-Up Book
ISBN: 1-56971-129-1 $17.95

Shadows of the Empire
ISBN: 1-56971-183-6 $17.95

The Empire Strikes Back—
The Special Edition
ISBN: 1-56971-234-4 $9.95

Return of the Jedi—The Special Edition
ISBN: 1-56971-235-2 $9.95

NEW REPUBLIC ERA:
5-25 YEARS AFTER
STAR WARS: A NEW HOPE

X-Wing Rouge Squadron
The Phantom Affair
ISBN: 1-56971-251-4 $12.95

Battleground Tatooine
ISBN: 1-56971-276-X $12.95

The Warrior Princess
ISBN: 1-56971-330-8 $12.95

Requiem for a Rogue
ISBN: 1-56971-331-6 $12.95

In the Empire's Service
ISBN: 1-56971-383-9 $12.95

Blood and Honor
ISBN: 1-56971-387-1 $12.95

Masquerade
ISBN: 1-56971-487-8 $12.95

Mandatory Retirement
ISBN: 1-56971-492-4 $12.95

Shadows of the Empire
Evolution
ISBN: 1-56971-441-X $14.95

Heir to the Empire
ISBN: 1-56971-202-6 $19.95

Dark Force Rising
ISBN: 1-56971-269-7 $17.95

The Last Command
ISBN: 1-56971-378-2 $17.95

Dark Empire
ISBN: 1-59307-039-X $16.95

Dark Empire II
ISBN: 1-56971-119-4 $17.95

Empire's End
ISBN: 1-56971-306-5 $5.95

Boba Fett—Death, Lies, & Treachery
ISBN: 1-56971-311-1 $12.95

Crimson Empire
ISBN: 1-56971-355-3 $17.95

Crimson Empire II—Council of Blood
ISBN: 1-56971-410-X $17.95

Jedi Academy—Leviathan
ISBN: 1-56971-456-8 $11.95

Union
ISBN: 1-56971-464-9 $12.95

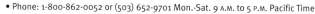

NEW JEDI ORDER ERA:
25+ YEARS AFTER
STAR WARS: A NEW HOPE

Chewbacca
ISBN: 1-56971-515-7 $12.95

INFINITIES:
DOES NOT APPLY TO TIMELINE

Infinities — A New Hope
ISBN: 1-56971-648-X $12.95

Infinities—The Empire Strikes Back
ISBN: 1-56971-904-7 $12.95

Infinities—Return of the Jedi
ISBN: 1-59307-206-6 $12.95

Star Wars Tales Volume 1
ISBN: 1-56971-619-6 $19.95

Star Wars Tales Volume 2
ISBN: 1-56971-757-5 $19.95

Star Wars Tales Volume 3
ISBN: 1-56971-836-9 $19.95

Star Wars Tales Volume 4
ISBN: 1-56971-989-6 $19.95

STAR WARS®
CLONE WARS
ADVENTURES

Don't miss any of the action-packed adventures of your favorite **STAR WARS**® characters, availble at comics shops and bookstores in a galaxy near you!

Volume 1
ISBN: 1-59307-243-0 / $6.95

Volume 2
ISBN: 1-59307-271-6 / $6.95

Volume 3
ISBN: 1-59307-307-0 / $6.95

Volume 4
ISBN: 1-59307-402-6 / $6.95

To find a comics shop in your area, call 1-888-266-4226
For more information or to order direct: • On the web: darkhorse.com • E-mail: mailorder@darkhorse.com
• Phone: 1-800-862-0052 or (503) 652-9701 Mon.-Sat. 9 A.M. to 5 P.M. Pacific Time
*Prices and availability subject to change without notice